METHUEN'S MONOGRAPHS
ON BIOCHEMICAL SUBJECTS

General Editors: SIR RUDOLPH PETERS, F.R.S.
and F. G. YOUNG, F.R.S.

BILE SALTS

BILE SALTS

G. A. D. HASLEWOOD
Professor of Biochemistry
at Guy's Hospital Medical School, London

METHUEN & CO LTD
11 NEW FETTER LANE · LONDON EC4

First published 1967
© 1967 *G. A. D. Haslewood*
Printed in Great Britain by
Richard Clay (The Chaucer Press), Ltd.,
Bungay, Suffolk

Distribution in the U.S.A.
by Barnes & Noble, Inc.

FOR BETH

Contents

General Editors' Foreword

Methuen's Biochemical Monographs are similar in form and aim to the series of Methuen's Monographs on other subjects. These books can be regarded as chapters of a large work which records progress in biochemistry in general, each volume aiming to provide an authoritative survey of a particular aspect of the subject. They are written in such a way that an introduction to the topic is provided both for students who are reaching the end of undergraduate studies and for research workers who wish to read about a subject cognate with their own. Although these books are written mainly for those who wish to study biochemistry, in practice they have proved to be attractive to a much wider group.

The volumes are intended to be handy and to be rather more than a review but less than a detailed monograph. They do not include a complete bibliography, but references are given which provide a key to the essential relevant literature.

As biochemistry widens its interest so the diversity of the subjects included in this series grows. The topics naturally range from some which are primarily chemical in emphasis to those which are essentially biological in outlook. Professor G. A. D. Haslewood has written a book which is a study both in chemistry and in comparative biology. In its chemical aspects it may be regarded as a companion volume to *The Chemistry of the Steroids* by Professor W. Klyne in the present series. It surveys widely scattered publications, including much of Professor Haslewood's own authorship and provides many interesting links between them. It concludes, as is natural, with a consideration of the evolutionary implications of the information it contains. Biochemistry provides, for the study of genetics and evolution, information of many sorts, of which the comparative study of a series of related substances is fundamentally important. Professor Haslewood has written both a readable book and a valuable contribution to comparative biochemistry.

R. A. P.
F. G. Y.

Author's Preface

This small book is described as a monograph, but it cannot be taken to be a fully documented comprehensive account of the subject of its title. Rather it represents an attempt to survey the field as a whole, with as much experimental detail as may be thought enlightening to the general reader and as much bibliography as should suffice to guide those wishing to go more thoroughly into particular aspects of the subject. Only the Appendix claims to be comprehensive; I apologize to my readers for the many 'unpublished observations' quoted therein, but think the reader might prefer to have these in advance of detailed publication: the original records may of course be inspected.

For earlier bile salt history, H. Sobotka's two books *Physiological Chemistry of the Bile* (1937) and *Chemistry of the Sterids* (1938) published by Baillière, Tyndall & Cox have never been equalled and for work up to 1955 *Physiological Reviews*, **35**, 178, may be consulted. Metabolic studies on bile salts have received considerable impetus in recent years from the work of Professor Sune Bergström and his colleagues at Lund and Stockholm: two of these, Jan Sjövall and Henry Danielsson, have written reviews that cover more fully the work described in Chapters Three and Four respectively. The pioneer studies on chemical bile salt differences were done by the late Tayei Shimizu and his colleagues in Okayama; his one-time pupil Professor Taro Kazuno and his co-workers continue to make important contributions, mentioned in these pages, from Hiroshima.

In compiling this book I have had in mind a variety of readers: chemists, biochemists, physiologists, gastroenterologists, zoologists and students simply interested in learning something about the subject. I have had generous advice, especially from Dr James B. Carey, Jnr., of

Minnesota University Medical School and, on zoological matters, from Dr Garth Underwood of the British Museum (Natural History). This advice must not, however, be blamed for any faults in the present work; these are my own.

I thank Dr A. D. Cross and the Editorial Board of the *Biochemical Journal* for permission to reproduce Figure 3.4 and Mrs Gillian Lee for Figure 1.1. I especially thank Miss Ann Edleston for her patience in typing and preparation of the manuscript.

G. A. D. H.

CHAPTER ONE

Introduction: Functions of Bile Salts

1.1 Introduction

The bile has always been of special interest to a minority of students of physiology and biochemistry. Produced uniquely by liver cells in all vertebrates examined, it drains via the biliary canaliculi into the ductules, intrahepatic ducts, hepatic duct and finally into the upper part of the small intestine. In most birds and mammals and apparently in all vertebrates below their evolutionary level, a gall-bladder is also present. A largely diagrammatic representation of the arrangement in man is given in Fig. 1.1.

In this figure short arrows show that the bile enters the gall-bladder (G), is discharged into the intestine at a junction (controlled by a sphincter: the sphincter of Oddi) usually shared by the point of entry of the pancreatic juice and thence travels down the small intestine (D, J, etc.). Certain biliary constituents, particularly the bile salts, are absorbed from the small intestine into the portal venous vessels and returned to the liver to be again excreted with the bile: this is the *enterohepatic circulation*. A proportion of the material so circulating escapes into the large intestine and reaches the faeces.

Physiologically, bile is to be regarded partly as a means of excretion, particularly of fats (including cholesterol) and of the breakdown products of haemoglobin (the bile pigments) and partly as a digestive secretion containing substances (phospholipids, especially lecithins, and bile salts) capable of aiding the digestion and absorption of fat and perhaps of other components of the diet. The enzyme alkaline phosphatase is present in high concentration in the bile of several mammalian species but no function has been clearly assigned to it.

1

It is not known whether the cellular mechanisms for excretion of bile pigments etc. and secretion of bile salts are distinct anatomically, but since cholesterol and fatty acids are essentially insoluble in water it can be supposed that the detergent properties of lecithins and bile salts play

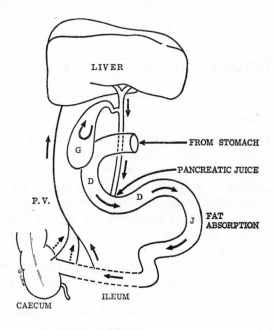

G.   Gall bladder
D.   Duodenum
J.   Jejunum
P.V. Portal venous system

Fig. 1.1 *The enterohepatic circulation (based on the arrangement in man).*

an important part in keeping such compounds in solution in the bile. For some time it was thought that the small amount of biliary protein might be important in this respect, but it now seems that the phospholipids, particularly lecithins, form micelles of definite composition with the cholesterol etc. and that such micelles may be further stabilized by the bile salts (Desai *et al.*, 1965; Norman, 1965; Neiderhiser *et al.*, 1966). Thus, the bile normally retains in solution all the substances passed into it by the liver cells: viz. mucin, protein, lipids, bile pigments (as their glucuronides in man at least), phospholipids and bile salts, together with alkaline phosphatase and perhaps traces of other enzymes and also inorganic ions (see Table 6.1, p. 59).

The gall-bladder has been shown, in a number of animal forms, to concentrate hepatic bile by using metabolic energy to reabsorb sodium and chloride ions and water in isotonic proportions (Diamond, 1965).

1.2 Functions of bile salts and other detergents

It seems from what has been said that perhaps the bile salts are not so important as phospholipids in keeping fats, including cholesterol, in solution in the bile itself. However, the situation in the duodenum is quite different. Here the bile salts certainly play a primary part in emulsification of the dietary fat prior to its digestion by pancreatic lipase. As triglyceride digestion proceeds (Fig. 1.2), the fatty acids released, having a pK in the region of 4·8, will act as soaps to a large extent at the duodenal pH (thought to be in man about 6·5) and so improve the emulsifying power of the system. The monoglycerides produced by lipase action also have distinct detergent properties. A powerful emulsifying agent is formed by removal of a fatty acid moiety from a molecule of lecithin by pancreatic phospholipase A to give lysolecithin. Further splitting of this by phospholipase B and possibly other enzymes in the pancreatic and intestinal secretions may cause the breakdown of this substance, so that its role in intestinal fat solubilization is uncertain.

$$
\begin{array}{lll}
\alpha\ CH_2 \cdot O \cdot COR_1 & CH_2 \cdot O \cdot COR_1 & \\
\beta\ CH \cdot O \cdot COR_2 \xrightarrow[\text{H}_2\text{O}]{\text{lipase}} & CH \cdot O \cdot COR_2 & +\quad R_3COOH \\
\alpha\ CH_2 \cdot O \cdot COR_3 & CH_2OH & \\
\text{Triglyceride} & \alpha,\beta\text{-Diglyceride} & +\quad \text{Fatty acid}
\end{array}
$$

$$
\xrightarrow[\text{H}_2\text{O}]{\text{lipase}}
\begin{array}{l}
CH_2OH \\
CH \cdot O \cdot COR_2 \quad +\quad R_1COOH \\
CH_2OH \\
\beta\text{-Monoglyceride} + \text{Fatty acid}
\end{array}
$$

Fig. 1.2   *Action of lipase.*

There is also good evidence that at pH 6·5 bile salts have an activating effect on pancreatic lipase, although the mechanism of this effect is unknown.

Thus, as digestion proceeds, the following substances with detergent properties are available to assist in fat solubilization: fatty acid ions, monoglycerides, lysolecithins, bile salts.

There has been, and still is, controversy about the form in which fat (mainly fatty acids, mono- and di-glyceride with a little undigested tri-glyceride) is finally absorbed, but the idea that 'particulate absorption' occurs to any great extent is not well supported. A spherical particle of 0·1–0·5 $\mu^\star$ in diameter contains millions of molecules of fat and would require special mechanisms for its transfer to the interior of the cells bordering the villi of the small intestine. It has been suggested that pinocytosis (a sort of phased engulfing) by these cells may account for the absorption of minor proportions of fat, but present opinions favour the view that subdivision into micelles must occur before general absorption. A 'micelle' in this sense is a group of from a few to perhaps thousands of molecules arranged so that the fatty, hydrocarbon-like, non-polar parts are together in the interior, while the water-attracting polar parts are in the aqueous surrounding medium. Detergent molecules such as soaps and bile salts are characteristically composed of both fatty and polar parts, and their molecules clump to form micelles in water at all but great dilutions: such micelles will be negatively charged at pH 6·5 and this will further increase their tendency to disperse. The micelles concerned in fat absorption will have $-OH$ groups (from mono- and di-glycerides), $-COO^-$ and $-COOH$ groups (from fatty acids and bile salts), and $-SO_3^-$ groups (from bile salts) on the outside and so will also bear negative charges. Borgström (1965) has suggested that bile salts micelles, if spherical and in a 0·15M solution of sodium taurocholate, might have diameters of about 16–20 Å. One may conceive that macromolecules of this size could be absorbed without detectable special mechanisms.

Fat absorption is efficient; in man it is thought to occur chiefly in the jejunum (Fig. 1.1), while the bile salts are in some unknown way liberated from the micelles to be absorbed lower down the small intestine, particularly in the lower ileum (Senior, 1964; Dietschy *et al.*, 1966).

$\star$ 1 μ (10^{-3} mm) = 10,000 Å.

After absorption there is resynthesis of triglycerides from fatty acids and also from mono- and di-glycerides, so that little but triglyceride fat is found in the lacteals draining into the lymphatic circulation. Fatty acids with a chain-length less than 14 carbon atoms tend, with decreasing chain-length, to be absorbed to a greater extent as free ions or molecules into the portal circulation.

From what has been said, the reader will perhaps have gathered that bile salts are thought to be of physiological importance in: (1) solubilizing fats, including cholesterol, in the bile itself, (2) causing the initial emulsification of dietary fat, (3) assisting in the action of pancreatic lipase and (4) stabilizing the micelles in which the digested fat is absorbed.

In addition, experimental findings support the views that bile salts: (5) in some way favourably influence the re-synthesis of triglycerides in the intestinal mucosa (Saunders & Dawson, 1963; Knoebel & Ryan, 1963), (6) are important in promoting the absorption of calcium from the small intestine (Webling & Holdsworth, 1966) and (7) by an uncoupling action on oxidative phosphorylation by liver mitochondria, act as regulators of the oxidative steps by which the cholesterol side-chain loses 3 carbon atoms in the formation of C_{24} bile acids (Lee & Whitehouse, 1965).

Thus there is ample experimental evidence and plenty of stimulating thought to encourage those who would like to take a greater interest in these substances, whose persistence in various chemical forms throughout the vertebrate world is a certain indicator of their importance in animal physiology.

REFERENCES

Desai, J. C., Glover, J. & Joo, C. N. (1965), Diamond, J. M. (1965) and Norman, A. (1965) refer to articles in *The Biliary System*. Ed. W. Taylor. Oxford: Blackwell.
Borgström, B. (1965) *Biochim. biophys. Acta*, **106**, 171.
Dietschy, J. M., Salomon, H. S. & Siperstein, M. D. (1966) *J. clin. Invest.*, **45**, 832.
Knoebel, L. K. & Ryan, J. M. (1963) *Am. J. Physiol.*, **204**, 509.
Saunders, D. R. & Dawson, A. M. (1963) In *Biochemical Problems of Lipids*. Ed. A. C. Frazer. Amsterdam: Elsevier.
Senior, J. R. (1964) *J. Lipid Res.*, **5**, 495.
Lee, M. J. & Whitehouse, M. W. (1965) *Biochim. biophys. Acta*, **100**, 317.
Neiderhiser, D. H., Roth, H. P. & Webster, L. T., Jr. (1966) *J. Lab. clin. Med.* **68**, 90.
Webling, D. D'A. & Holdsworth, E. S. (1966) *Biochem. J.*, **100**, 652.

B

CHAPTER TWO

Chemistry

2.1 The C_{24} bile acids

The fundamental work on the structure of the commoner bile acids (summarized by Sobotka, 1938 and Fieser & Fieser, 1949; 1959) appeared to show that these substances were all (with the chemically understandable exception of 3α-hydroxy-6-oxoallocholanic acid – see Table 2.1) hydroxyl or keto derivatives of cholanic acid (5β-cholan-24-oic acid), $C_{24}H_{40}O_2$ (1).

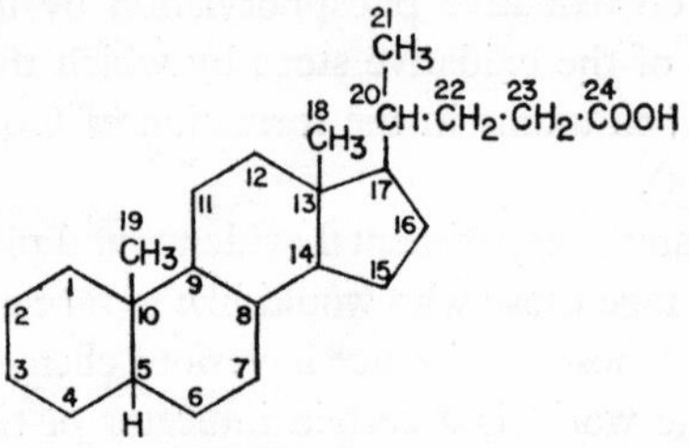

(1) Cholanic acid

In this acid the configuration at C-5 is 'β', i.e. *cis* to the methyl group at C-10; the stereochemistry of the rest of the molecule is the same as it

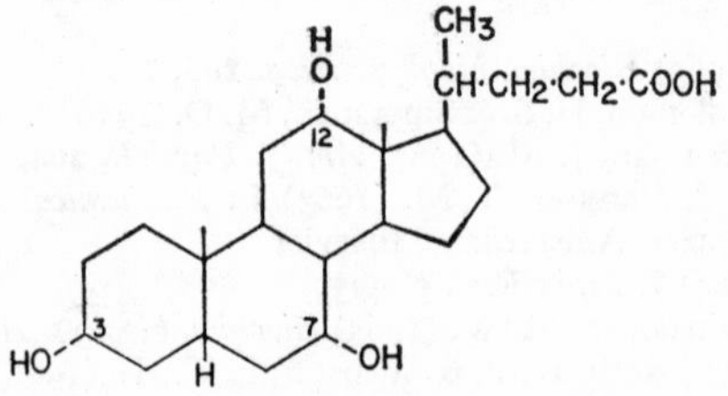

(2) Cholic acid

is in cholesterol. Naturally occurring bile acids have been found with hydroxyl as substituent at C-3, C-6, C-7, C-12, C-16 and C-23. The commonest bile acid is cholic acid (2), in which the three −OH groups at C-3, C-7 and C-12 are all 'α' (i.e *trans.* to the C-10 methyl group). Names and formulae of other C_{24} acids from biles are shown in Table 2.1).

3α,12α-Dihydroxy-7-oxocholanic acid has been found in the bile of a python, a monkey and domestic cattle; 7α,12α-dihydroxy-3-oxo-, 3α-hydroxy-7,12-dioxo- and 3α-hydroxy-12-oxocholanic acid were also found in cattle bile (see Appendix).

Other cholanic acid derivatives have been found in faeces and some at least are artifacts made by intestinal microflora from the common bile acids. Faecal bile acids are listed in Table 2.2 and further discussed in Chapters Five and Six.

It was thought until quite recently that only the 5β acids occurred in bile. This idea seemed to be supported by the obviously suitable 'detergent' shape of the molecule conferred by this configuration (see below). However, investigations into the chemistry of an acid originally called 'tetrahydroxynorsterocholanic acid' and first isolated by Ohta (1939) from the Japanese 'Gigi' fish (*Pelteobagrus nudiceps* Sauvage) showed that this compound was actually a 2 : 1 (w/w) mixture of allo-cholic and cholic acids. Allocholic acid (3) is the 5α epimer of cholic acid (Anderson & Haslewood, 1962).

(3) Allocholic acid, m.p. 241°, [α]$_D$ +23°

Allocholic acid occurs as a high proportion of the bile acids in some lizards and in lesser amounts in teleostean fish, snakes, birds and mammals; the quantities so far detected in mammalian bile are very small. Allodeoxycholic acid (3α,12α-dihydroxyallocholanic acid) has been isolated from rabbit bile and faeces (Tables 2.1 and 2.2) and its

Cholanic acid derivatives

(e.a. denotes an artifact of the entero-

Name of acid isolated from bile	Hydroxyl groups at	[a] Approx. m.p.(°)	[b] Approx. $[\alpha]_D(°)$
3α,7α,12α,23ξ-Tetra hydroxycholanic		Amorphous	+36 [c]
Bitocholic	3α,12α,23ξ	Amorphous	+48
Cholic	3α,7α,12α	198	+37
Hyocholic	3α,6α,7α	189	+5
α-Muricholic	3α,6β,7α	200	+38
β-Muricholic	3α,6β,7β	226	+61
Phocaecholic	3α,7α,23ξ	225	+11
Pythocholic	3α,12α,16α	187	+28 [d]
Chenodeoxycholic	3α,7α	c. 140 (solvated)	+11
Deoxycholic	3α,12α	177 (usually solvated)	+53
Hyodeoxycholic	3α,6α	197	+5
'β' Lagodeoxycholic		218	+37
Ursodeoxycholic	3α,7β	203	+57
3α,6β-Dihydroxycholanic		210	+37
3β,6α-Dihydroxycholanic		190	+5
3α-Hydroxy-6-oxoallo(5α)cholanic		194	−9 [e]
3α-Hydroxy-7-oxocholanic		203	−27
Lithocholic	3α	186	+35
3-Oxochola-4:6-dienic		152	

[a] Melting points are often dependent on the solvents used for crystallization; most bile acids are solvated in the crystal structure and some (e.g. deoxycholic acid) form definite compounds with solvents and other substances (Ref. [4]).

[b] Rotations in ethanol, except as indicated.

[c] Ethyl ester.

[d] Methyl ester hydrate, in chloroform.

[e] In chloroform.

isolated from bile
hepatic circulation (see Chapter Five))

Source of bile	Remarks	References to chemistry
Seals; some snakes	Perhaps Hammarsten's (1909; 1910) 'α-phocaecholic acid'	[1, 6]
Some snakes	Probably e.a.	[6]
Most evolutionarily advanced vertebrate groups	The commonest bile acid	[3, 4]
Pigs (*Sus*)		[4]
Rats; mice		[8]
Rats; mice		[8]
Seals, sea-lions, walruses	Formerly called 'β phocaecholic'	[4, 6]
Boid snakes	Easily forms a lactone; partly e.a.	[4]
Many evolutionarily advanced vertebrates	A principal bile acid in some mammals (including man) and some birds	[4]
Substantial amounts only from mammals	E.a. from cholic acid	[3]
Pigs (*Sus*); wart hog	E.a. from hyocholic	[4]
Rabbit	Now known to be 3α,12α-di-hydroxyallocholanic acid	[2, 3, 9, 12]
Many mammals, in small amounts	Partly or sometimes e.a.	[4]
Domestic pig	Probably e.a.	[10]
Domestic pig, especially in gallstones	Probably e.a.	[4, 7]
Domestic pig	Probably in bile as 5β isomer, itself e.a.	[4]
Many mammals; some birds	Sometimes e.a. Formerly called 'nutriacholic acid'	[4]
Some mammals; pig gallstone	E.a. from chenodeoxycholic	[4]
Domestic fowl	Probably in bile as 7-hydroxy-3-oxo-4-cholenic	[11]

REFERENCES

[1] Bergström, S., Krabisch, L. & Lindeberg, U. G. (1959) *Acta Soc. Med. Upsalien.*, **64**, 160.
[2] Danielsson, H., Kallner, A. & Sjövall, J. (1963) *J. biol. Chem.*, **238**, 3846.
[3] Fieser, L. F. & Fieser, M. (1949) *Natural Products Related to Phenanthrene*, 3rd Edn. New York: Reinhold.
[4] Fieser, L. F. & Fieser, M. (1959) *Steroids*. New York: Reinhold.
[5] Hammarsten, O. (1909; 1910) *Hoppe-Seyl Z.*, **61**, 454; **68**, 109.

Continued at foot of next page

10   *Bile Salts*

biogenesis is discussed in Chapter Four. Allochenodeoxycholic acid (3α,7α-dihydroxyallocholanic acid) has not so far been found in substantial amounts in nature. Since allocholic acid is present in the bile of germ-free chicks and chenodeoxycholic acid is the major bile acid in these animals, it was supposed that a search for allochenodeoxycholic acid might be successful; however, it is now clear that if this acid occurs at all in germ-free chick bile it is only in very minor proportions.

The C_{24} acids mentioned above occur naturally as conjugates in bile (see below), or in faeces, gallstones and enteroliths as free acids or ions. Numerous esters and other derivatives have been prepared and described. Sobotka (1938) gives a useful earlier catalogue and a newer one is that of Van Belle (1965); search for references to more recently investigated substances can be made in *Chemical Abstracts* and similar works.

Deoxycholic acid forms quite stable 'choleic acids', as mentioned in Table 2.1 and these may be isolated from natural sources. For instance, jejunal enteroliths from elderly people usually consist chiefly of a readily crystallizable deoxycholic acid–fatty acid complex (approx. 8:1, w/w), melting at about 187°. Cholic acid and chenodeoxycholic acids are present in small proportion in such intestinal stones, but after surgical interference cholic acid can be a major constituent of stones in an intestinal loop (see Chapter Six).

In addition to the acids listed in Tables 2.1 and 2.2, a number of other substituted cholanic acids of the 5α and 5β configuration have been made in the laboratory and some have been obtained by biosynthesis from other bile acids; these are further discussed in Chapter Four. Some of these laboratory-made cholanic acids are listed in Table 2.3.

Oxidation of the secondary hydroxyl groups in bile acids leads to the corresponding ketones, referred to as 'dehydro' compounds. Thus (4)

[6] Haslewood, G. A. D. (1961) *Biochem. J.*, **78**, 352.
[7] Haslewood, G. A. D. & Wootton, V. (1950) *Biochem. J.*, **47**, 584.
[8] Hsia, S. L., Elliott, W. H., Matschiner, J. T., Doisy, E. A., Jr., Thayer, S. A. & Doisy, E. A. (1960) *J. biol. Chem.*, **235**, 1963.
[9] Hofmann, A. F. & Mosbach, E. H. (1964) *J. biol. Chem.*, **239**, 2813.
[10] Ratliff, R. L., Matschiner, J. T., Doisy, E. A., Jr., Hsia, S. L., Thayer, S. A., Elliott, W. H. & Doisy, E. A. (1961) *J. biol. Chem.*, **236**, 685.
[11] Wiggins, H. S. (1955) Ph.D. Thesis Univ. London.
[12] Yukawa, M. (1962) *Hiroshima J. med. Sci.*, **11**, 167.

TABLE 2.2

Bile acids isolated from or detected in faeces

Bile acid	Species	Principal references
Cholanic	Man	[1]
Lithocholic	Man, rabbit, rat, dog	[1, 2, 3, 4, 5, 7, 8]
3β-Hydroxycholanic	Man, rabbit	[2, 3, 4, 5]
7β-Hydroxycholanic	Man	[1]
3-oxocholanic	Man	[5]
Chenodeoxycholic	Dog, man	[1, 5, 8]
Ursodeoxycholic	Man	[1, 5]
3β,7α-Dihydroxycholanic	Man	[5]
3α,12α-Dihydroxyallocholanic	Rabbit (see Table 2.1)	[4]
Deoxycholic	Man, rabbit, rat, dog	[1, 2, 3, 4, 5, 7, 8]
3α,12β-Dihydroxycholanic	Man	[1, 5]
3β,12α-Dihydroxycholanic	Man, rabbit	[1, 2, 3, 4, 5]
3β,12β-Dihydroxycholanic	Man	[1, 5]
3α-Hydroxy-7-oxocholanic	Man	[1, 5]
3α-Hydroxy-12-oxocholanic	Man, rabbit, rat, dog	[1, 2, 3, 4, 5, 8]
3β-Hydroxy-12-oxocholanic	Man, rabbit	[2, 3, 4, 5]
7α-Hydroxy-3-oxocholanic	Man	[5]
12α-Hydroxy-3-oxocholanic	Man	[1, 5]
3,12-Dioxocholanic	Man	[5]
Cholic; allocholic; 3β,7α,12α– and 3α,7β,12α–trihydroxycholanic; 3α,12α–dihydroxy-7-oxocholanic	Dog	[8]
Cholic; allocholic; 3β,7α,12α–, 3β,7β,12α– and 3α,7β,12α–trihydroxycholanic; 3α,7α–dihydroxy-12-oxo– and 3α,12α–dihydroxy-7-oxocholanic	Man	[6]

REFERENCES

[1] Ali, S. S., Kuksis, A. & Beveridge, J. M. R. (1966) *Can. J. Biochem.* **44,** 957.

[2] Danielsson, H., Eneroth, P., Hellström, K., Lindstedt, S. & Sjövall, J. (1963) *J. biol. Chem.,* **238,** 2299.

[3] Danielsson, H., Eneroth, P., Hellström, K. & Sjövall, J. (1962) *J. biol. Chem.,* **237,** 3657.

[4] Danielsson, H., Kallner, A. & Sjövall, J. (1963) *J. biol. Chem.,* **238,** 3846.

[5] Eneroth, P., Gordon, B., Ryhage, R. & Sjövall, J. (1966) *J. Lipid Res.,* **7,** 511.

[6] Eneroth, P., Gordon, B., & Sjövall, J. (1966) *J. Lipid Res.,* **7,** 524.

[7] Fieser, L. F. & Fieser, M. (1959) *Steroids.* New York: Reinhold.

[8] Hirofuji, S. (1965) *J. Biochem. Tokyo,* **58,** 27.

TABLE 2.3

Some laboratory-made C₂₄ acids

Name of acid	Remarks	References
3α,6β,7β,12α-Tetrahydroxycholanic		[8]
3α,7β,12α-Trihydroxyallocholanic		[1]
3β,7α,12α-Trihydroxyallocholanic		[2]
3α,6α,7β-Trihydroxycholanic	'ω-muricholic acid': made by rats from hyodeoxycholic acid and by surgically jaundiced mice from chenodeoxycholic acid	[6, 12]
3α,6α,12α-Trihydroxycholanic	Formerly claimed to be made from Ohta's (1939) acid	[4] (1959)
3α,6β,12α-Trihydroxycholanic	Made by surgically jaundiced rats from deoxycholic acid	[10]
3β,7α,12α-Trihydroxycholanic		[5]
3α,7β,12α-Trihydroxycholanic	Made by rat liver from 3α,12α-dihydroxy-7-oxocholanic acid	[11]
3α,7α,12β-Trihydroxycholanic		[5]
3α,11α,12α-, 3α,11α,12β-, 3α,11β,12α- and 3α,11β,12β-Trihydroxycholanic		[4] (1949)
3α,6β- and 3β,6β-Dihydroxyallocholanic		[13]
3β,6β-, 3α,11α-, 3α,11β-, 3α,12β-, 7α,12α, 11α,12α- and 11α,12β-Dihydroxycholanic		[4] (1949)
3β,12β-Dihydroxycholanic		[3]
6β,7α- and 6β,7β-Dihydroxycholanic		[8]
3α and 3β-Hydroxyallocholanic; 6α-, 7α-, 11β-, 12α-, and 12β-hydroxycholanic		[4] (1949)
6β-Hydroxycholanic		[7]

REFERENCES

[1] Anderson, I. G. & Haslewood, G. A. D. (1962) *Biochem. J.*, **85**, 236.
[2] Anderson, I. G. & Haslewood, G. A. D. (1964) *Biochem. J.*, **93**, 34.
[3] Chang, F. C., Wood, N. F. & Holton, W. G. (1965) *J. org. Chem.*, **30**, 1718.
[4] Fieser, L. F. & Fieser, M. (1949; 1959); *see* references to Table 2.1.
[5] Hasegawa, K. (1959) *Hiroshima J. med. Sci.*, **8**, 271.
[6] Hsia, S. L., Elliott, W. H., Matschiner, J. T., Doisy, E. A., Jr., Thayer, S. A. & Doisy, E. A. (1960) *J. biol. Chem.*, **235**, 1963.
[7] Jones, D. & Summers, G. H. R. (1959) *J. chem. Soc.*, p. 2594.

Continued at foot of next page

(4) Dehydrocholic (3,7,12-trioxocholanic) acid, m.p. 237°, $[\alpha]_D$ +27°

is dehydrocholic acid. Similarly, dehydrochenodeoxycholic (3:7-dioxocholanic, m.p. 160°, $[\alpha]_D$ −27°) and dehydrodeoxycholic (3:12-dioxocholanic, m.p. 187°, $[\alpha]_D$ +92°) acids are easily prepared. With 6-hydroxy cholanic acids, oxidation to the ketone (5) is followed, in the presence of excess of OH⁻ or H_3O^+, by allomerization to the more stable 5α (allo) forms (7), presumably as a result of enolization from C-5 (formula (6)). This allomerization is not, however, complete (Jones &

(5)   (6)   (7)

Kime, 1966). A similar mechanism, accompanied by a ketol transformation of the kind well known at C-11/C-12 (Fieser & Fieser, 1959), probably accounts for the nature of the products (partial formula (9)) of hot alkaline hydrolysis of esters of 3α-acetoxy-6α-bromo-7-oxocholanic acid (partial formula (8)) and their 12α-hydroxy derivatives. In this case the thermodynamically more probable 7β (equatorial)

[8] Kagan, H. B. & Jacques, J. (1960) *Bull. soc. Chim.*, p. 871.

[9] Ohta, K. (1939) *Hoppe-Seyler's Z.*, **259**, 53.

[10] Ratliff, R. L., Matschiner, J. T., Doisy, E. A., Jr., Hsia, S. L., Thayer, S. A., Elliott, W. H. & Doisy, E. A. (1961) *J. biol. Chem.*, **236**, 685.

[11] Samuelsson, B. (1960) *Acta chem. Scand.*, **14**, 17.

[12] Ziboh, V. A., Hsia, S. L., Matschiner, J. T., Doisy, E. A., Jr., Elliott, W. H., Thayer, S. A. & Doisy, E. A. (1963) *J. biol. Chem.*, **238**, 3588.

[13] Ziegler, P. (1959) *Can. J. Chem.*, **37**, 1004.

(8)   (9)

hydroxyl group results from the ketol rearrangement. The 7β-hydroxy-6-oxo-5α-cholanic acids (9) are thus formed and this reaction provides a useful route to both allocholic and allodeoxycholic acids (Anderson & Haslewood, 1964; Yukawa, 1962; Hofmann & Mosbach, 1964).

Enolization of C-4 ketones likewise gives rise to 5α compounds from the 5β series.

Selective oxidation of secondary hydroxyl groups can be brought about chemically and also enzymically. With cholic acid, chromic oxidation leads successively to the C-7 monoketone, the C-7 and C-12 diketone and finally to (4). N-Bromosuccinimide gives selective oxidation at C-7 (Fieser & Fieser, 1959) or C-6 (Jones & Summers, 1959), and aluminium t-butoxide oxidizes selectively at C-3 (Jones *et al.*, 1949). The group most easily oxidized by potassium chromate/acetic acid in 3α,7β,12α-trihydroxyallocholanic acid, in which C-3α is axial and C-7β equatorial, was found to be that at C-12α (axial). N-Bromosuccinimide oxidation of this acid, however, gave a preponderance of the C-7 ketone (Anderson & Haslewood, 1962), as with the 5β,7α isomer (cholic acid).

The products of reduction of ring keto groups depend on the reagents used. Metal hydride reduction gives chiefly the equatorial alcohols, but with sodium–alcohol and catalytic hydrogenation conditions can often be found to yield axial isomers, sometimes predominantly (Fieser & Fieser, 1959). For instance, 3-oxocholanic acids can be hydrogenated to give the 3β (axial) alcohols (Danielsson *et al.*, 1962).

Partial acylation is affected by steric factors. Thus, the hindered 12α hydroxyl group resists acetylation with cold acetic anhydride/pyridine (Fieser & Fieser, 1959) and so does the C-7 hydroxyl group (α or β) when it is hindered by a hydroxyl group at C-6α, but not when C-6 is CH_2 (Haslewood, 1956; Hsia *et al.*, 1958). Bulkier acyl groups can be used to effect substitution at C-3 only (Fieser & Fieser, 1959).

Partial alkaline hydrolysis or acid alcoholysis of the C-3α acetoxy group is easily achieved; C-12α acetoxy is markedly more resistant to alkaline hydrolysis than acetoxy at C-3, C-6 or C-7 (Fieser & Fieser, 1959).

The ketocholanic acids can be brominated; removal of HBr then leads to unsaturated substances, as does dehydration of the hydroxy acids. The products can be hydroxylated with OsO_4, peroxides or other reagents or can be hydrogenated to yield deoxy acids. Kishner–Wolff or Huang–Minlon reduction of ketones can usually be used also to make these deoxy compounds. Dehydration of cholic acid with zinc chloride leads to a mixture, one component of which is the curious apocholic acid (10), containing a C_8–C_{14} double bond. This unsaturated linkage is inert to most reagents and cannot be catalytically hydrogenated (Fieser & Fieser, 1959). Apocholic acid shares with deoxycholic acid the property of forming choleic acids.

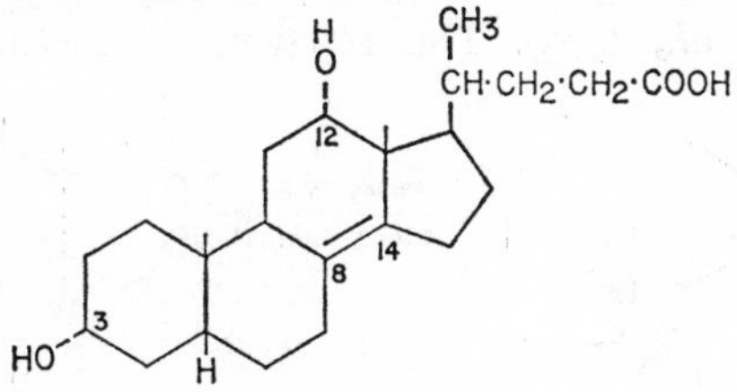

(10) Apocholic acid

The bile acid side chain is shortened by the Wieland–Barbier or Meystre–Miescher methods (Fieser & Fieser, 1959), leading to the nor (11) and bisnor (12) acids, the ketones (13) and aetianic acids (14).

(11) $R \cdot CH(CH_3) \cdot \overset{23}{CH_2} \cdot COOH$ 24-nor

(12) $R \cdot CH(CH_3) \cdot \overset{22}{COOH}$ 24,23-bisnor

(13) $R \cdot CO \cdot \overset{21}{CH_3}$

(14) $R \cdot \overset{20}{COOH}$ aetianic acids

(R = bile acid nucleus)

Side chains have been lengthened by the Arndt–Eistert reaction, by malonic ester condensation and by anodic synthesis; by such methods, substances with the nucleus (R) of cholic acid and with side chains as in (15)–(18) have been prepared (Bridgwater, 1956; Fieser & Fieser, 1959).

(15) $R \cdot CH(CH_3) \cdot CH_2 \cdot CH_2 \cdot \overset{25}{CH_2} \cdot COOH$ \qquad 25-homo

(16) $R \cdot CH \cdot (CH_3) \cdot CH_2 \cdot CH_2 \cdot \overset{26}{CH_2} \cdot CH_2 \cdot COOH$ \qquad 25,26-bishomo

(17) $R \cdot CH(CH_3) \cdot CH_2 \cdot CH_2 \cdot \overset{25}{CH_2} \cdot CH(CH_3)_2$

(18) $R \cdot CH(CH_3) CH_2 \cdot CH_2 \cdot CH_2 \cdot \overset{28}{CH}(CH_3) CH_2 \cdot COOH$

A curious reaction recently explored is the conversion, in poor and capricious yield, of a 5β, C-3 ketone to the corresponding 5α compound by prolonged boiling with Raney nickel in cumene (isopropylbenzene). For instance, methyl 12α-hydroxy-3-oxocholanate (partial formula (19)) gave the 5α ketone (20), which in turn furnished both $3\alpha,12\alpha$-dihydroxy-allocholanic (allodeoxycholic) and $3\beta,12\alpha$-dihydroxyallocholanic acids (Danielsson *et al.*, 1963). This reaction, the mechanism of which

(19) \qquad\qquad (20)

is unknown, was described for other steroids by Chakravarti *et al.* (1962) and has also been used to make $3\beta,7\alpha,12\alpha$-trihydroxyallocholanic acid (Anderson & Haslewood, 1964).

Many other reactions of steroids in general can be used to effect alterations in the bile acid molecule (see Van Belle, 1965).

2.2 C_{28} and C_{27} bile acids

A list of these isolated from biles is given in Table 2.4.

The chemistry of $3\alpha,7\alpha,12\alpha$-trihydroxycoprostanic ($3\alpha,7\alpha,12\alpha$-tri-hydroxy-5β-cholestan-26 (or 27)-oic) acid (21) is well understood. Both epimers at C-25 have been isolated from frog biles; however, the process entailed prolonged heating in aqueous alkali and may have caused some epimerization at C-25. Undoubtedly other C_{27} acids exist in the bile of various species of fishes, reptiles and amphibians.

TABLE 2.4

Naturally occurring bile acids with more than 24 carbon atoms

Name of acid	Suggested formula	Source (bile)	Remarks	References
Trihydroxybufosterocholenic	$C_{28}H_{46}O_5$	Toad, *Bufo vulgaris japonicus*	Unsaturated. May be 24-methyl-$3\alpha,7\alpha,12\alpha$-trihydroxycoprost-22-enic acid	[5]
Tetrahydroxysterocholanic Tetrahydroxyisosterocholanic	$C_{27}H_{46}O_6$ $C_{27}H_{46}O_6$	Chelonia (turtles, tortoises)	Both form lactones. One is probably $3\alpha,7\alpha,12\alpha,22\xi$-tetra-hydroxycoprostanic acid	[1]; unpublished observations
Varanic	$C_{27}H_{46}O_6$	Lizards of family Varanidae	Probably $3\alpha,7\alpha,12\alpha,24\xi$-tetra-hydroxycoprostanic acid	[2]
Two acids	$C_{27}H_{46}O_6$	Eel, *Anguilla japonica*	Both form lactones and have the cholic acid nucleus	[6]
$3\alpha,7\alpha,12\alpha$-Trihydroxycoprostanic	$C_{27}H_{46}O_5$	Crocodilia; species of frogs (*Rana*); man	See text	[4]
$3\alpha,7\alpha,12\alpha$-Trihydroxy-25α-coprost-23-enic	$C_{27}H_{44}O_5$	*Bufo vulgaris japonicus*	Hydrogenated to the corresponding coprostanic acid	[4]
$3\alpha,7\alpha$-Dihydroxycoprostanic	$C_{27}H_{46}O_4$	*Alligator mississipiensis*		[3]

REFERENCES

[1] Amimoto, K., Hoshita, T. & Kazuno, T. (1965) *J. Biochem.*, Tokyo, **57**, 565.
[2] Collings, B. G. & Haslewood, G. A. D. (1966) *Biochem. J.*, **99**, 50P.
[3] Dean, P. D. G. & Whitehouse, M. W. (1966) *Biochem. J.*, **99**, 9P.
[4] Fieser, L. F. & Fieser, M. (1959) *Steroids*. New York: Reinhold.
[5] Hoshita, T., Sasaki, T., Tanaka, Y., Betsuki, S. & Kazuno, T. (1965) *J. Biochem.*, Tokyo, **57**, 751.
[6] Okada, S., Masui, T., Hoshita, T. & Kazuno, T. (1962) *J. Biochem.*, Tokyo, **51**, 310.

(21) 3α,7α,12α-Trihydroxycoprostanic acid

2.3 Conjugates of bile acids

In eutherian mammals, C_{24} bile acids are found conjugated with glycine (formula (22)) as well as with taurine (23); in the rest of the animal kingdom only taurine conjugates have been identified. Except

$$R \cdot CO \cdot NH \cdot CH_2 \cdot COOH \qquad R \cdot CO \cdot NH \cdot CH_2 \cdot CH_2 \cdot SO_3H$$

(22) Glycine conjugate   (23) Taurine conjugate

possibly in frogs, toads and turtles (e.g. Amimoto *et al.*, 1965), not more than traces of free bile acids have been found in biles from healthy animals, although they do occur in gallstones, enteroliths and faeces.

Glycine and taurine conjugates can be prepared as described by Fieser & Fieser (1959). However, whatever the method of preparation, the conjugates are difficult to free from unconjugated bile acids. Taurocholic acid is fairly easily freed from cholic acid (Anderson, 1962) but countercurrent distribution methods are probably necessary to purify glycine conjugates in bulk.

2.4 The bile alcohols

In amphibians and some fishes the bile salts include alcohols, present as their sulphate esters. Some of these alcohols are listed in Table 2.5. In all cases, except that of myxinol, the monosulphate esters, $R \cdot O \cdot SO_3^-$, are found in the bile salts, with Na^+ and K^+. In 1898 Olof Hammersten reported the presence of substances of this kind in shark bile and isolated a crystalline compound, which he called 'α-scymnol', after alkaline hydrolysis of the bile salts. Elucidation of the chemistry of this showed that it had the cholic acid nucleus and a side chain containing an oxide ring. The following formula was suggested:

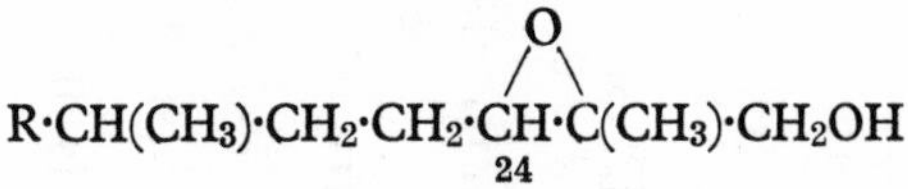

$$\overset{\displaystyle O}{\overset{\displaystyle \diagup\diagdown}{R{\cdot}CH(CH_3){\cdot}CH_2{\cdot}CH_2{\cdot}\underset{24}{CH}{\cdot}C(CH_3){\cdot}CH_2OH}}$$

'α-Scymnol' (R = cholic acid nucleus)

However, Fieser & Fieser (1949; 1959) proposed that the oxide ring should be regarded as 4-membered and put forward the structure (24).

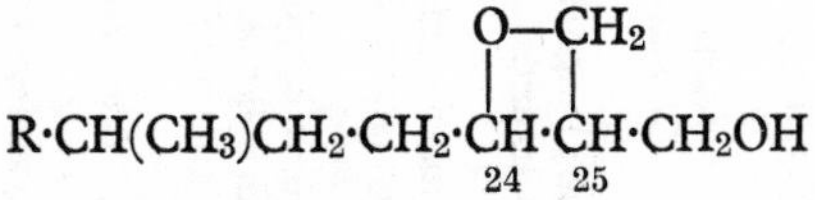

$$\overset{\displaystyle O{-}CH_2}{\overset{\displaystyle |\quad\ |}{R{\cdot}CH(CH_3)CH_2{\cdot}CH_2{\cdot}\underset{24}{CH}{\cdot}\underset{25}{CH}{\cdot}CH_2OH}}$$

(24) Anhydroscymnol

This structure was shown by Cross (1960, 1961) to be entirely correct; Cross's work was a striking illustration of the application of physical methods (especially nuclear magnetic resonance measurements) to structural problems and it gave a new impetus to the study of bile alcohols. It had been found also that (24) was an artifact of the alkaline hydrolysis and when the parent bile alcohol was obtained Cross suggested that this be called 'scymnol' and 'α-scymnol' be renamed 'anhydroscymnol'. Scymnol sulphate is (25). Anhydro bile alcohols are formed

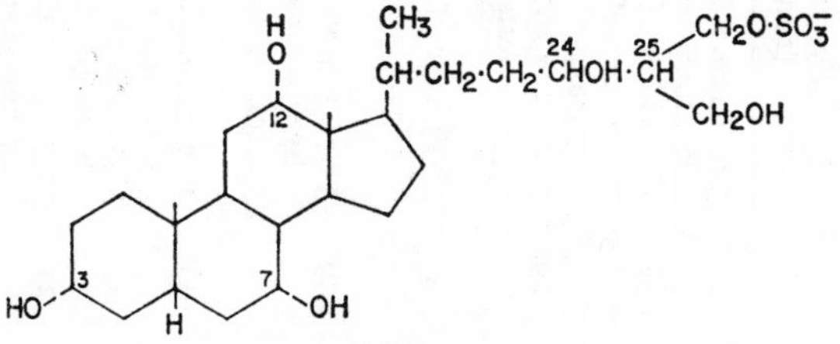

(25) Scymnol sulphate

also after alkaline hydrolysis of the sulphates of chimaerol, cyprinol, latimerol and ranol. They arise by elimination of sulphate ion between the $-O{\cdot}SO_3^-$ group and a suitably placed $-OH$ group. All these anhydro substances are substituted trimethylene oxides, like (24), and their formation can be written:

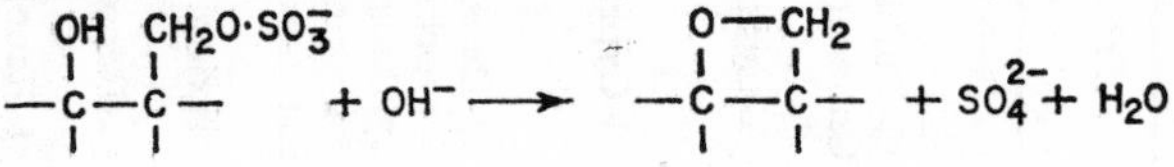

$$\overset{OH\ \ CH_2O{\cdot}SO_3^-}{\overset{|\quad\ |}{-C-C-}}\ +\ OH^- \longrightarrow\ \overset{O-CH_2}{\overset{|\quad\ |}{-C-C-}}\ +\ SO_4^{2-}+\ H_2O$$

TABLE 2.5

Bile alcohols

Trivial name	M.p.°	[α]D°	Systematic name (text formula)	Source (bile)	References
5α-Bufol			3α,7α,12α,25ξ,26 (or 27)-Pentahydroxy-5α-cholestane	Newt, *Diemyctylus pyrrhogaster*	[13]
5β-Bufol	178	+38	5β-Epimer of above (30)	Toad, *Bufo vulgaris japonicus*	[17]
Chimaerol	182	+41·5	3α,7α,12α,24ξ,26 (or 27)-Pentahydroxy-5β-cholestane (26)	Rabbit fish, *Chimaera monstrosa*	[4]
5α-Cyprinol	244	+29	3α,7α,12α,26,27-Pentahydroxy-5α-cholestane (see (28))	Cyprinid fish; lungfish, *Protopterus*; coelacanth, *Latimeria chalumnae*	[1, 10]
5β-Cyprinol	173		5β-Epimer of above	Frog, *Rana nigromaculata*; eel, *Conger myriaster*; Sturgeon, *Acipenser huso*	[5, 12, 16]
27-Deoxy-5α-cyprinol	232	+39	3α,7α,12α,26 (or 27)-Tetrahydroxy-5α-cholestane	Carp, *Cyprinus carpio*; Toad, *Bufo vulgaris japonicus*	[11, 14]
27-Deoxy-5β-cyprinol[a]	201		5β-Epimer of above	Toad, *Bufo vulgaris japonicus*	[14]
Latimerol[a]	236	+33	3β,7α,12α,26,27-Pentahydroxy-5α-cholestane	Coelacanth, *Latimeria chalumnae*	[2]
Myxinol[b]	204	-15	3β,7α,16α,26 (or 27)-Tetrahydroxy-5β-cholestane (see27))	Hagfish (Myxinidae)	[5, 9]
5α-Ranol	Amorphous	+21	3α,7α,12α,24ξ,26-Pentahydroxy-27-nor-5α-cholestane (see 29))	Some frogs (Ranidae)	[8]
5β-Ranol	189		5β-Epimer of above	Some frogs (Ranidae)	[15]
Scymnol[c]	123[a]	+34[a]	3α,7α,12α,24ξ,26,27-Hexahydroxy-5β-cholestane	Elasmobranchii (sharks and rays)	[3, 7]

a Identified after injection of ¹⁴C-4-cholesterol.

b Derived from the 3β,27-disulphate (27) occurring in the bile.

c The name 'α-scymnol' was given by O. Hammarsten to the substance now called 'anhydroscymnol' (see text).

d Dihydrate.

REFERENCES

[1] Anderson, I. G., Briggs, T. & Haslewood, G. A. D. (1964) *Biochem. J.*, **90**, 303.
[2] Anderson, I. G. & Haslewood, G. A. D. (1964) *Biochem. J.*, **93**, 34.
[3] Bridgwater, R. J., Briggs, T. & Haslewood, G. A. D. (1962) *Biochem. J.*, **82**, 285.
[4] Bridgwater, R. J., Haslewood, G. A. D. & Watt, J. (1963) *Biochem. J.*, **87**, 28.
[5] Cross, A. D (1966) *Biochem. J.*, **100**, 238.
[6] Cross, A. D., Landis, P. W. & Murphy, J. W. (1965) *Steroids*, **5**, 655.
[7] Fieser, L. F. & Fieser, M. (1959) *Steroids*, New York: Reinhold.
[8] Haslewood, G. A. D. (1964) *Biochem. J.*, **90**, 309.
[9] Haslewood, G. A. D. (1966) *Biochem. J.*, **100**, 233.
[10] Hoshita, T., Nagayoshi, S. & Kazuno, T. (1963) *J. Biochem.*, Tokyo, **54**, 569.
[11] Hoshita, T., Sasaki, T. & Kazuno, T. (1965) *Steroids*, **5**, 241.
[12] Hoshita, T., Yukawa, M. & Kazuno, T. (1964) *Steroids*, **4**, 569.
[13] Hoshita, T., Nagayoshi, S., Kouchi, M. & Kazuno, T. (1964) *J. Biochem.*, Tokyo, **56**, 177.
[14] Hoshita, T., Sasaki, T., Tanaka, Y., Betsuki, S. & Kazuno, T. (1965) *J. Biochem.*, Tokyo, **57**, 751.
[15] Kazuno, T., Masui, T. & Okuda, K. (1965) *J. Biochem.*, Tokyo, **57**, 75.
[16] Kazuno, T., Betsuki, S., Tanaka, Y. & Hoshita, T. (1965) *J. Biochem.*, Tokyo, **58**, 243.
[17] Okuda, K., Hoshita, T. & Kazuno, T. (1962) *J. Biochem.*, Tokyo, **51**, 48.

The trimethylene oxide ring gives a strong band (max 10·41 μ) in the infra-red spectrum, thus facilitating recognition of the anhydro compounds.

Chimaerol is probably 26-deoxyscymnol (26).

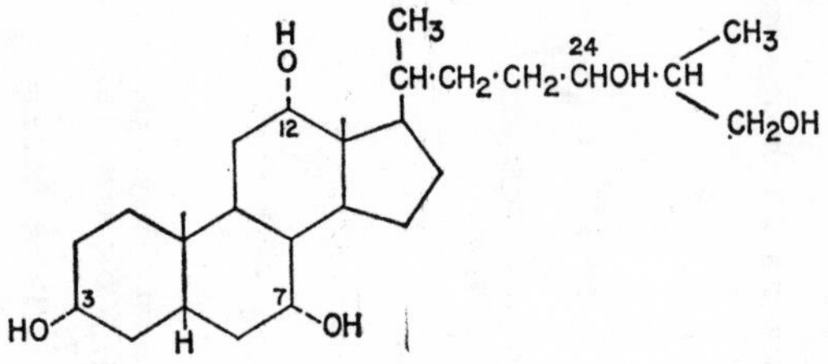

(26) Chimaerol

Myxinol disulphate is almost certainly (27).

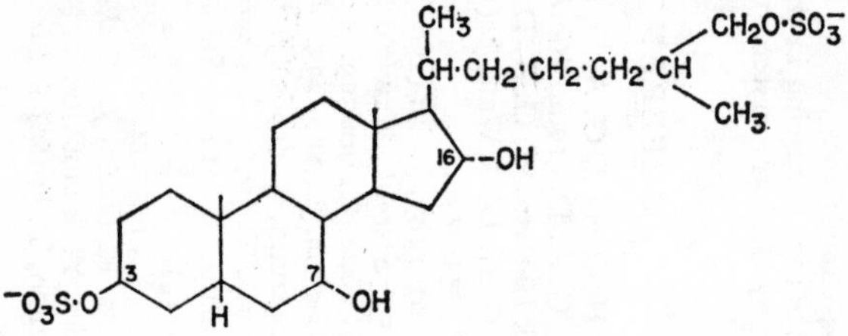

(27) Myxinol disulphate

Cyprinol sulphates are the 5α- and 5β-epimers of (28) and latimerol sulphate is the $3\beta,5\alpha$ epimer.

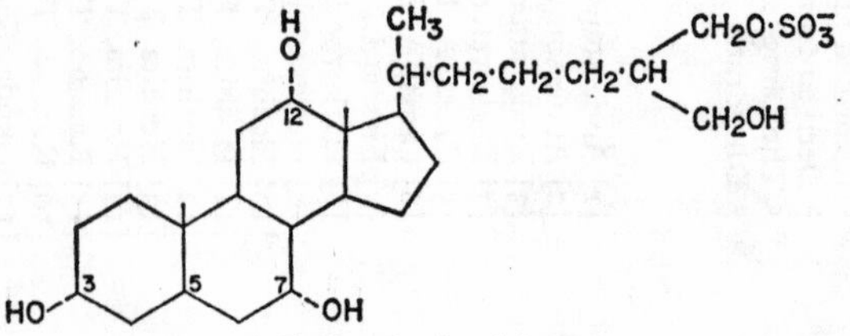

(28) Cyprinol sulphates

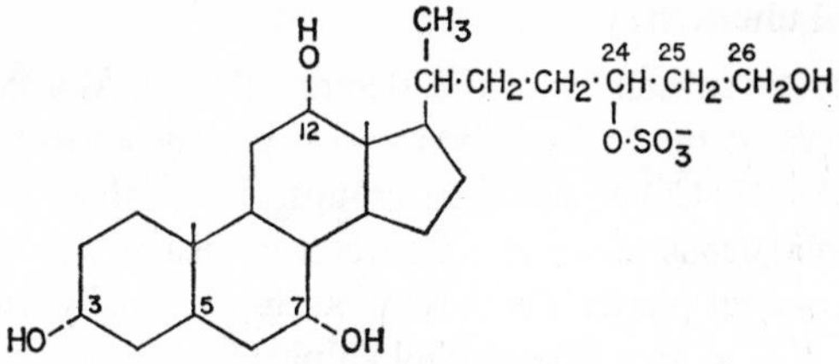

(29) Ranol sulphates

5α- and 5β-ranol sulphates have the structure (29).

A number of other compounds have been isolated after treatment of frog bile salts with alkali; these are artifacts whose chemistry has been elucidated (for references, see Haslewood, 1964).

Pentahydroxybufostane, a C_{28} alcohol obtained from toad bile by Kazuno and his colleagues (see Fieser and Fieser, 1949), is also an artifact of methods used in its isolation and the principal bile alcohol of the toad *Bufo vulgaris japonicus* is 5β-bufol (30).

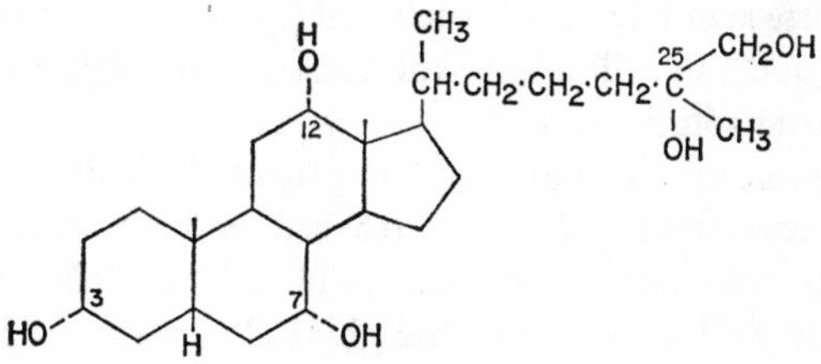

(30) 5β-Bufol

It is certain that other bile alcohols will be found in lower vertebrate forms; for example, small quantities of such substances, not identical with those listed in Table 2.5, occur in sturgeons' bile. Lamprey bile salts will probably be found to be of the alcohol sulphate type and it will be surprising if the bile alcohol is myxinol.

Chimaerol, 5β-cyprinol, 5β-ranol and scymnol have been made by partial synthesis. This task is likely to prove laborious for the allo(5α) compounds until a method for making allocholic acid in good yield is discovered. No conjugate, i.e. sulphate ester, of any bile alcohol has as yet been made in the laboratory, except by biosynthesis.

2.5 Physical chemistry

The bile salts are substances of the 'detergent' type. Molecular models show that most of the hydrocarbon part is clearly separated from the polar OH, COOH, COO^- and SO_3^- groups. Thus, these polar groups can lie in the aqueous phase of a fat/water emulsion, the hydrocarbon part lying in the fat phase. These remarks apply equally well to taurocholate (Fig. 2.1) as to a bile alcohol sulphate, such as ranol sulphate (Fig. 2.2). At physiological pH (say pH 6–8·5) taurine conjugates and sulphate esters will be present almost entirely as ions (pK of taurocholic acid about 1·4), i.e. $R \cdot SO_3^-$. At similar pH glycine conjugates exist as a mixture of ions $R \cdot COO^-$ and minor amounts of acids $R \cdot COOH$ (pK of glycocholic acid about 4·5). In aqueous solutions these ions and acid molecules will, at any but great dilution, be associated into *micelles* (particles containing from a few to perhaps thousands of molecules and ions), formed by clumping of the hydrocarbon parts of molecules and ions to form the interior of the micelles and dispersion of these particles in the aqueous medium by the water-attracting action of the external polar groups. In many cases also, the distribution of $-OH$ groups on the molecular surface of bile salts is such that hydration between them can easily occur and this will add to the tendency for dispersion to take place in aqueous solutions.

When bile salt solutions in water are progressively diluted a 'critical micellar concentration (CMC)' is reached and at dilutions greater than this the solutions are monomolecular. The CMC can be demonstrated by conductivity and other physical measurements. Recently there have been many studies on the physical state of bile salts and other detergents in conditions such as are thought to exist in the mammalian intestine (for references see, e.g., Hofmann & Borgström, 1962; Senior, 1964).

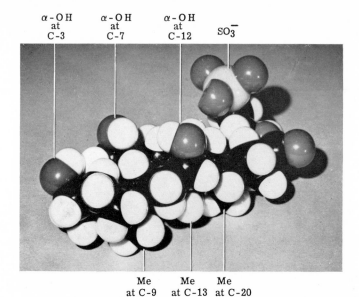

α-O H at C-3   α-O H at C-7   α-O H at C-12 SO_3^-

Me at C-9   Me at C-13   Me at C-20

Fig. 2.1 *Stuart type model of taurocholate* ($R \cdot CO \cdot NH \cdot CH_2 \cdot CH_2 \cdot SO_3^-$; $R \cdot COOH$ = *cholic acid (Formula (2)). Note how the polar groups lie on one side of the molecule. The three –OH groups are approximately equidistant, and a molecule of water can be arranged so as to bridge any two of them.*

SO_3^- at C-24   OH at C-26   α–OH at C-12   α–OH at C-7   α–OH at C-3

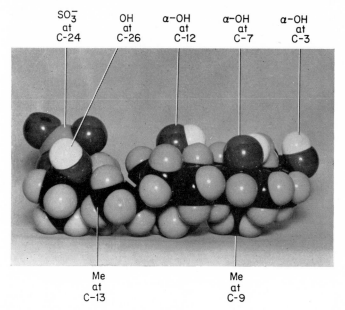

Me at C-13   Me at C-9

Fig. 2.2 *Stuart type model of 5α-ranol sulphate (Formula (29), 5α-H at C-5).*

REFERENCES

Amimoto *et al.* (1965) *see* Table 2.4.
Anderson, I. G. (1962) *Nature*, Lond., **193**, 60.
Anderson & Haslewood (1962; 1964) *see* Table 2.2.
Bridgwater, R. J. (1956) *Biochem. J.*, **64**, 593.
Chakravarti, D., Chakravarti, R. N. & Mitra, M. N. (1962) *Nature*, Lond., **193**, 1071.
Cross, A. D. (1960) *Proc. chem. Soc.*, Lond., p. 344.
Cross, A. D. (1961) *J. chem. Soc.*, p. 2817.
Danielsson *et al.* (1962) *see* Table 2.2.
Danielsson *et al.* (1963) *see* Table 2.1.
Fieser & Fieser (1949; 1959) *see* Table 2.1.
Haslewood, G. A. D. (1956) *Biochem. J.*, **62**, 637.
Haslewood (1964) *see* Table 2.5.
Hofmann, A. F. & Borgström, B. (1962) *Fed. Proc.*, **21**, 43.
Hofmann & Mosbach (1964) *see* Table 2.1.
Hsia, S. L., Elliott, W. H., Matschiner, J. T., Doisy, E. A. Jr., Thayer, S. A. & Doisy, E. A. (1958) *J. biol. Chem.*, **233**, 1337.
Jones & Summers (1959) *see* Table 2.3.
Jones, A. S., Webb, M. & Smith, F. (1949) *J. chem. Soc.*, p. 2164.
Jones, D. N. & Kime, D. E. (1966) *J. chem. Soc.* (C), p. 846.
Ohta (1939) *see* Table 2.3.
Senior (1964) *see* References to Chapter One.
Sobotka (1938) *see* Author's Preface.
Van Belle, H. (1965) *Cholesterol, Bile Acids and Atherosclerosis*. Amsterdam: North-Holland Publishing Co.
Yukawa (1962) *see* Table 2.1.

CHAPTER THREE

Methods of Isolation, Identification and Analysis

3.1 Isolation of bile salts

A crude preparation of bile salts can be obtained as follows.

(1) Bile is collected from a fistula or as soon as possible after death. The whole gall-bladder or bile is put into a large excess (at least five times the volume of bile) of 'absolute' or 95 per cent ethanol or 'absolute' methylated spirit (approx 95 per cent ethanol, 5 per cent methanol). Weaker (more aqueous) alcohols will probably suffice, but there should be no additives other than water. In these conditions bile salts will apparently keep indefinitely, although there may be post-mortem changes before the bile is collected.

(2) The alcoholic solution is filtered and the container and filter washed with 95 per cent ethanol. The precipitate (containing mucin, bile pigments, etc.) is discarded and the filtrate evaporated to dryness, finally in a dish on a boiling water-bath.

(3) The residue, dried over calcium chloride *in vacuo*, is extracted 3–4 times with light petroleum ('b.p. 40–60°'), the extract is filtered if necessary and the filter washed with light petroleum. The light petroleum extract contains most of the fats, including cholesterol, from the bile.

(4) The material insoluble in light petroleum is agitated with excess of methanol at room temperature. The methanolic solution is filtered and the containers, filters etc. are washed with methanol. Evaporation of the methanol leaves the bile salts as a more or less hygroscopic gum or powder that will keep for a long time in dry conditions.

The above sequence (1–4) provides a roughly *quantitative* estimation of bile salts in bile that has been so collected that it is uncontaminated by pieces of liver or other tissue. Step (3) excludes some fats and step (4) most of the inorganic salts. For quantitative work, in addition to the obvious necessity for complete collection of filtrates and washings, it is essential to dry the bile salts to constant weight. For this they may be put into a weighed bottle having a well-fitting stopper. The stopper and open bottle containing the bile salts are dried in a desiccator *in vacuo* over calcium chloride, etc. As soon as the desiccator is opened the stopper is inserted and the whole reweighed. The process is repeated until a constant weight is reached.

The petroleum extract in step (3) can be used to examine biliary fat; in this case the bile salts should be well triturated with the solvent to ensure as complete extraction of fat as possible. After evaporation of the extract, cholesterol can be estimated by one of the usual colorimetric methods: precipitation as digitonide is also suitable, since virtually all the cholesterol (in human bile at least) is free (not esterified). The fatty extract will also include phospholipids (present in human bile largely as lecithin), which can be estimated by a method for organically combined phosphate. Fatty acids in the extract can be methylated and analysed by gas-liquid chromatography.

The isolated bile salts may be examined for sulphate esters, taurine conjugates and glycine conjugates by paper or thin-layer chromatography, as described (**3.5**). Their complete separation on a preparative scale is not feasible except by elaborate counter-current distribution methods, but small amounts can be eluted from chromatograms and estimated by one of the methods described by Sjövall (1964).

3.2 Preparation of bile acids

The bile salts (or crude bile) can be hydrolysed in aqueous alkali without serious damage to most of the known C_{24} acids except when very small amounts are used, expecially in glass vessels (Sjövall, 1964). A common procedure is as follows:

(1) N g of bile salts are dissolved by warming (if necessary) in $10n$ ml of normal sodium or potassium hydroxide. The solution is sealed in a metal bomb or autoclave (a beaker of alkaline bile salt solution can be heated in an ordinary pressure cooker) and heated at $115-120°$ for 6–8 hours. For some as yet unknown reason, higher temperatures (140–

160°) are needed for complete hydrolysis of bile salts (e.g. pig bile salts) consisting principally of the conjugates of dihydroxy acids.

(2) The cooled autoclave is opened and the contents washed out with water. Any precipitate should be collected and examined, in case it represents bile alcohols. The filtered alkaline solution is acidified with dilute aqueous hydrochloric acid and an excess of solid sodium chloride is added. After refrigeration the precipitate is collected, thoroughly washed with water and dried *in vacuo* over calcium chloride or by evaporation with ethanol/benzene *in vacuo*.

The conjugates of the C_{27} acids (e.g. trihydroxycoprostanic acid; **2.2**) are resistant to hydrolysis, presumably because the acids contain a somewhat hindered carboxyl group, in the arrangement $-\overset{25}{C}H(CH_3)COOH$. The drastic conditions used to hydrolyse conjugates of these acids may result in epimerization at C-25 and in other molecular changes.

The final aqueous acidic filtrate should be tested for sulphate ion by the addition of 0·5M barium chloride if bile alcohols are suspected or sought.

The isolated bile acids can be examined by paper, thin-layer or gas-liquid chromatography (Sjövall, 1964; Sandberg *et al.*, 1965). They can be esterified with diazomethane or diazoethane in methanol or ethanol, or as follows: *n* g of dried bile acids are dissolved at room temperature in 10*n* ml of 2 per cent (v/v) sulphuric acid–methanol, –ethanol, –propanol, etc. After standing overnight at room temperature the mixture is diluted with aqueous sodium bicarbonate and extracted three times with ether. The ether is washed with water, dried and evaporated. Acidification of the bicarbonate liquors precipitates unesterified acids.

The esters can be examined for keto (oxo) compounds by a Girard separation (e.g. Haslewood, 1954) and can be separated on alumina or silicic acid (Sjövall, 1964).

In some cases the crude bile acids can be crystallized directly from ethyl acetate. This solvent is of great value in purifying bile acids and alcohols, for polymeric material which sometimes appears to be formed during the hydrolysis procedures is insoluble in ethyl acetate. A few extractions with the hot solvent will usually remove all bile acids, and evaporation of the filtered extract leaves a much improved product.

Some workers prefer to extract precipitated material directly with ethyl acetate from the acidified products of hydrolysis.

3.3 Preparation of bile alcohols

Bile alcohols appear as precipitates insoluble in the alkali used for hydrolysis as described above. However, this hydrolysis is known to cause alterations in almost all bile alcohols so far investigated (see Chapter Two) and bile salts to be examined for bile alcohols should be treated in other ways, e.g. by acid hydrolysis or dioxan–trichloroacetic acid cleavage.

ACID HYDROLYSIS. This can be done in 0·25N hydrochloric acid as described, for example, by Anderson *et al.* (1964) and is suitable for the preparation of 5α-ranol or of 5α-cyprinol.

DIOXAN–TRICHLOROACETIC ACID CLEAVAGE. The method was described by Cohen & Oneson (1953) for steroid hormone sulphates and has proved very valuable for bile alcohols. The sulphates are partially acetylated and then cleaved at room temperature with a solution of dry trichloroacetic acid (2–40%, w/w) in dry dioxan (e.g. Haslewood, 1964). Scymnol is partially decomposed by this technique if the concentration of trichloroacetic acid exceeds 2 per cent; this concentration is sufficient for the cleavage of scymnol sulphate in shark bile.

3.4 Chromatography

The methods for this have been well reviewed, with experimental details, by Sjövall (1964), whose article should be consulted by those intending to work in this field. What follows here is a brief summary, with a few details supplementary to Sjövall's account.

ALUMINA AND SILICA. Alumina can be neutralized and re-activated, as described by Shoppee (1949) or Evans & Shoppee (1953), and may then be used, in 10–50 times the weight of material to be separated, for the purification on columns of bile acid esters, bile alcohols or their acyl derivatives. A useful general order of eluting solvents is: benzene, ether, acetone, ethanol, with mixtures of each with increasing proportions of the next in succession. Other solvents have been described (Sjövall, 1964).

Silica gel has some advantages over alumina for absorption chromatography.

Absorption chromatography is valuable as a preparative method, especially on a large scale, but rarely gives completely pure products.

CELITE AND OTHER COLUMN PARTITION MATERIALS. Columns made up in celite will hold the more polar ('stationary') phase of equilibrated solvent mixtures and the bile salts, acids, alcohols or esters can be applied to the column and eluted by the less polar ('moving') phase. About 100 mg require about 10 g of celite, holding approximately 5 ml of stationary phase. The method is capable of giving very pure products, without decomposition, and the efficiency of separation depends on the solvent system used and the length of the column. Carpenter & Hess (1956) give a theoretical treatment. A useful and versatile solvent system for neutral substances (bile acid esters and bile alcohols) is ethanol–water, 80 per cent v/v, as stationary phase and mixtures of heptane* and benzene as moving phase (e.g. Haslewood, 1964). Proportions of benzene can be varied from 0 to 85 per cent (v/v).

If celite is made hydrophobic by treatment with dimethyldichlorosilane it will then hold the less polar phase and can be used for 'reversed phase' partition chromatography. A commercial polythene powder, 'Hostalen S', can also be used for this purpose. Full details are given by Sjövall (1964).

PAPER CHROMATOGRAPHY. Most solvent systems in use for this have 70 per cent v/v acetic acid : water as the nominal stationary phase. This is established by washing the paper in the phase and drying it for a few minutes at about 100°. Equilibration in tanks, etc., is then carried out in the usual way. This washing and drying technique has given improved results with all solvent systems used in the author's laboratory.

For taurine conjugates and alcohol sulphates the system amyl acetate† : heptane : acetic acid : water, 17 : 3 : 21 : 10 (v/v) used in descending chromatography is very convenient. It is a modification of one of Sjövall's (1955) systems.

---

* Light petroleum, b.p. 80–100°, redistilled over solid potassium hydroxide is suitable.

† 'Confectionary grade,' redistilled, b.p. 141–2°, is suitable.

For glycine conjugates and free bile acids, mixtures of di-isopropyl ether and heptane (1 : 9 to 17 : 3, v/v) as moving phase and 70% v/v acetic acid : water as stationary phase give good separations (Sjövall, 1964).

Bile acid esters and acetates of alcohols can conveniently be separated on paper with the systems of Bush (1952), especially his 'A' and 'B₃'.

After such separations the papers are dried and then dipped in a 10 per cent w/v solution of phosphomolybdic acid in ethanol (Kritchevsky & Kirk, 1952). A few minutes heating at 100° reveals the substances as blue spots. This development technique fails with keto acids and esters, unless there is also a hydroxyl group other than at C-3; e.g. it does not reveal 3α-hydroxy-7-oxocholanic acid and its esters.

For hydroxy acids, a solution of antimony trichloride in chloroform, used as a dip and followed by heating and viewing under a Woods lamp, will reveal these as characteristically fluorescent spots that are useful for identification (Carey & Bloch, 1954).

Sjövall (1964) has used fluorescence in sulphuric acid of materials eluted after paper chromatography as a method of quantitative estimation of bile acids, and reviews the work of others. Paper chromatography can be used preparatively (e.g. Haslewood, 1954).

THIN-LAYER CHROMATOGRAPHY (TLC). This is very useful in this as in other fields and provides rapid results. 'Silicagel G' (Merck), is a suitable absorbent, and spots can be developed by heating after spraying with phosphomolybdic acid, aqueous sulphuric acid or uranyl nitrate (5 per cent, w/v) in 10 per cent (v/v) sulphuric acid/water.

Solvent systems for bile alcohols and acids and their derivatives, including conjugates, have been described (Sjövall, 1964). In the author's experience TLC is most valuable as a test for purity of samples, but is rather less reliable than paper chromatography for identification; there seems to be some mutual interference between substances in mixtures that sometimes prevents them running at the same rate as standards on TLC plates.

GAS–LIQUID CHROMATOGRAPHY (GLC). Sjövall (1964) has carefully studied the use of this technique for bile acids and alcohols, usually as their esters. The advantages are that a few micrograms are sufficient for analysis and that with proper techniques very satisfying separations can be achieved. On the other hand, the equipment is expensive and needs skilled attention. It should be understood, of course, that this is still only a chromatographic separation; identity of retention times for substances on a GLC column no more guarantees chemical identity than does the same R_F value in a paper or TLC separation. Where there is no doubt about chemical identity, for example as to bile acids in human blood, then GLC methods surely offer the most satisfactory analysis (e.g. Sandberg *et al.*, 1965).

Sjövall (1964) reviews methods of *glass–paper chromatography*, which appears to be a useful technique, and also describes *electrophoresis* and *ion-exchange chromatography*.

3.5 Quantitative estimation

Apart from the approximate general method outlined in **3.1**, quantitative analysis has been applied only to the more common C_{24} bile acids and their conjugates. As mentioned above, GLC is likely to prove the method of choice for these and even the complex mixture of faecal bile acids may, when all its components have been identified, be resolved by this method.

Colour reactions such as the Pettenkofer, Liebermann–Burchardt and others involving the use of concentrated sulphuric or phosphoric acids with the addition of other compounds have been used for the estimation of various bile acids; some details are given by Sjövall (1964), who also describes the use for quantitative analysis of the fluorescence caused by bile acids and sulphuric acid in different conditions. As he remarks, great care is needed to reach satisfactory analytical standards with any of the methods, especially when small quantities such as are found in blood are concerned.

3.6 Colour reactions

HAMMARSTEN TEST. Bile acids and alcohols having hydroxyl groups in the 3α or 3β, 7α, and 12α or (probably) 12β positions often respond to the very useful Hammarsten test. This is done by gently heating the substance (about 1–5 mg) with concentrated (approx. 10N) aqueous hydrochloric acid over a small flame for a few moments, afterwards allowing the mixture to stand, with occasional shaking, for about an hour. A positive response is yellow→green→purple or blue and may be complete or partial. A purple colour is given by cholic, allocholic and 3β,7α,12α-trihydroxy-cholanic and -allocholanic acids and their esters or conjugates, by apocholic, 3-oxo-7α,12α-dihydroxycholanic and 3α,7α,12α,23-tetrahydroxycholanic acids and their esters, and by the bile alcohols scymnol, chimaerol, latimerol, cyprinol and ranol and their naturally occurring sulphates. The nature of the side-chain has a considerable effect; thus, 24-norcholic acid (11) gives a purplish-green, 23,24-bisnorcholic acid (12), a green and the ketone (13) (formulae, p. 15, R = cholic acid nucleus) a yellow colour.

Lengthening the side-chain, perhaps by adding non-polar groups that decrease solubility in the reagent, diminishes the response, unless extra side-chain hydroxyl groups are added also. For example, 3α,7α,12α-trihydroxycoprostanic acid (formula, p. 18) gives a feeble or negative response, but varanic acid and the (probably) 3α,7α,12α,22ξ-tetrahydroxycoprostanic acid from turtle biles give purple colours. Anhydroscymnol, having a terminal $-CH_2OH$ group (formula, p. 19) gives a positive response, but anhydro-chimaerol, -cyprinol and -ranol do not. The test is valuable in preparative work, as a rough assay method, and also as a guide in the study of new substances of the bile acid or alcohol type. I do not favour a modification in which the substance to be tested is first dissolved in acetic acid, for this obscures observation of whether it will dissolve, wholly or partially, in the hydrochloric acid and whether a precipitate afterwards appears. These phenomena are of value for identification and, with practice, are useful guides even when one is dealing with compounds that do not give definite colours in the test.

THE PETTENKOFER TEST. Although the point has never been systematically investigated, it is possible that this test, one of whose modifications is described by Sjövall (1964), may yield similar information to that given by the Hammarsten test.

THE LIEBERMANN–BURCHARDT TEST. This well-known steroid test (e.g. Cook, 1958) gives only a rather feeble result, unless a 16α-hydroxyl group or a nuclear double bond is present.

3.7 Infra-red spectroscopy

Infra-red absorption spectra of bile salts, acids and alcohols can conveniently be observed in a nujol mull or in potassium bromide disks; such polar substances are not usually appreciably soluble in chloroform or carbon disulphide. As mentioned in Chapter Two, most bile salt derivatives strongly adhere to solvents, which cannot always be removed by prolonged drying at temperatures below the melting-point. For making disks, therefore, the substances are dissolved in minimal amounts of a suitable solvent (e.g. methanol, ethanol, acetone) and a few drops of the solution containing an appropriate weight of solute are added to powdered KBr in a small mortar. After drying at about 45° the KBr is repowdered and the disk prepared in the usual way.

Characteristic infra-red patterns are given by some substituted steroid ring-systems and are of great value for recognition. Wootton (1953) first pointed out that the cholic acid nucleus could be recognized in all derivatives tested (other than taurine conjugates), and I have found this to be true of numerous acids and alcohols. The spectrum of molecules having the cholic acid nucleus (Fig. 3.1) has a characteristic pattern in the region 9·0–11·0 μ; bands are prominent at about (maximum) 9·3, 9·6, 10·2, 10·5 and 10·95 μ (see also Fischmeister, 1960). These peaks, and especially the broad complex band with maximum at about 9·6 μ, are obvious features in all substances so far examined

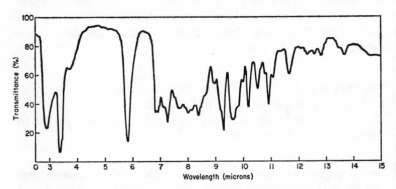

Fig. 3.1   *Infra-red spectrum of cholic acid in potassium bromide:
Perkin-Elmer Infracord Instrument.*

having an unsubstituted cholic acid nucleus and a side chain not containing sulphur.

The resemblance between the infra-red spectra of some alcohols and acids having the cholic acid nucleus but different side chains is very close; the only obvious features of difference are the relative intensities of some of the bands.

The nucleus of allocholic acid (formula, p. 7) also shows features that have been readily recognized in bile alcohols and other derivatives. Absorption bands with maxima at about 9·2, 9·7, 9·9, 10·4 and 11·2 μ are very prominent in the spectrum (Fig. 3.2). The double peak with maxima at about 9·7 and 9·9 μ and also the band with maximum about 11·2 μ are especially valuable for recognition of 3α,7α,12α-trihydroxyallo steroids.

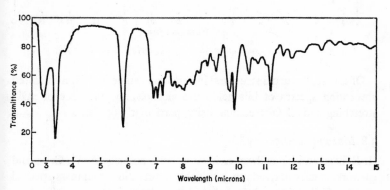

Fig. 3.2   *Infra-red spectrum of allocholic acid. Details as Fig. 3.1.*

However, the spectra of substances having this nucleus are by no means so closely similar as those of compounds with that of cholic acid.

Other nuclei can be detected by infra-red spectroscopy (Fischmeister, 1960), for example, that of 3β,7α,12α-trihydroxyallocholanic acid was found in latimerol (p. 22), and a first step in the examination of a new bile acid or alcohol should be a comparison of its infra-red spectrum with that of known compounds.

The trimethylene oxide ring found in anhydro bile alcohols (p. 19) can be recognized by the greatly increased absorption at about 10·4 μ (Cross, 1960), which usually blends with the peaks at 10·5 and 10·4 μ

in substances having the cholic or allocholic acid nucleus respectively to give a broad strong peak. The other features mentioned above of the cholic and allocholic acid spectra are not affected. As an example, Fig. 3.3 shows the infra-red spectrum of 5α-anhydrocyprinol.

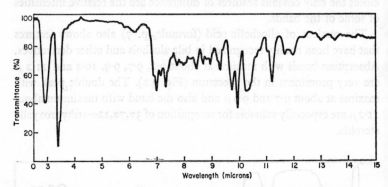

Fig. 3.3   *Infra-red spectrum of 5α-anhydrocyprinol. Details as Fig. 3.1.*

Of course, the usual structural information can be had from infra-red absorption spectra of bile acids and alcohols, the presence of –OH stretching and ⫶C=O stretching being particularly obvious.

3.8 Mass spectroscopy

R. Ryhage and his colleagues in Stockholm and also A. D. Cross and co-workers have derived much valuable information from mass-spectral studies of bile acids and alcohols and their derivatives.

A common feature is a peak at m/e 253, which is attributed to a triply unsaturated hydrocarbon ion, $C_{19}H_{25}^+$, derived by loss of the side chain and of three molecules of water or of acetic acid from the substituted steroid nucleus: thus, this peak is found in the mass spectra of steroids having three nuclear hydroxyl or acetoxyl groups, or two such groups and a nuclear double bond.

Even when a peak at m/e corresponding to the molecular ion is not seen, it may be possible to deduce the molecular weight. For example, Cross (1964) compared the mass spectra of 5α-cyprinol and 5α-ranol tetra-acetates (Fig. 3.4) and showed that the principal peaks (m/e above 400) of the ranol derivative were 'at m/e ratios consistently lower by

14 mass units than their counterparts in the spectrum of cyprinol tetra-acetate'. Since there was good reason to believe that the molecular weight of 5α-cyprinol tetra-acetate was 620, that of 5α-ranol tetra-acetate was assessed as 606, an important point in deciding the remarkable formula (29) for ranol sulphate.

3.9 Nuclear magnetic resonance (NMR)

Cross (1960) initiated the use of NMR for the elucidation of the structure of anhydroscymnol as described on p.19. Infra-red spectroscopy revealed that this substance had a trimethylene oxide ring (formula, p. 19), and Cross then reduced it with lithium aluminium anhydride, thus obtaining a compound which NMR measurement showed contained the unit $-CH(CH_3)CH_2OH$. The new compound was therefore 26-deoxyscymnol (formula, p. 22). The experience gained was put to good use in a study of 5α-cyprinol and 5α-ranol tetra-acetates. The NMR spectrum of cyprinol tetra-acetate revealed the unit $-CH(CH_2OCOCH_3)_2$ and confirmed formula (28) (p. 22) for 5α-cyprinol sulphate. 5α-Ranol tetra-acetate gave an NMR spectrum similar in many respects, but at $5\cdot93\tau$ a 2-proton multiplet was attributed to 'two magnetically equivalent protons immediately adjacent to acetate in the environment $CH_2 \cdot CH_2 \cdot O \cdot CO \cdot CH_3$'. This observation excluded the possibility of the presence of more than one carbon atom on C-25, and strongly supported the C_{26} formula (29) for 5α-ranol (Cross, 1964). NMR spectroscopy can provide evidence for structural features of bile acid and alcohol molecules that could hardly be obtained by chemical means with the amounts of material available, and its application to steroids has been discussed in detail by Bhacca & Williams (1964). An especially valuable way of using the method is by a consideration of the (algebraically) additive effects of various alterations in the steroid ring-system on the chemical shifts given by the resonances of the protons in the methyl groups at C-10 and C-13 (C-19 and C-18 protons).

3.10 Optical rotation measurements

No hypothesis for the structure for a bile acid or alcohol or any derivative can be maintained unless it can be reconciled with the specific

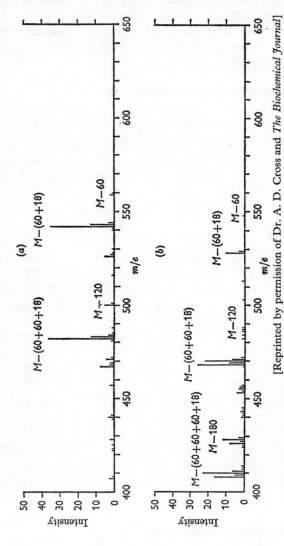

Fig. 3.4 *Mass spectra of: (a) cyprinol tetra-acetate, and (b) ranol tetra-acetate. Mass spectra are represented only for m/e ratios above 400. Peak intensities are expressed as a percentage of the most intense peak in the spectrum (m/e 253 for both compounds). Peaks with an intensity of less than 1 per cent of the strongest peak are not shown.*

[Reprinted by permission of Dr. A. D. Cross and The Biochemical Journal] optical rotation as calculated from known examples. In some cases, for example the assignment of the third ⁻OH group in pythocholic acid and in myxinol to C-16α (Tables 2.1 and 2.5), an important reason for supporting a formula is the value of $[\alpha]_D$.

Nevertheless, there is clearly room for more optical studies in this field and some stereochemical problems, for instance the configuration of the side-chain hydroxyl groups in 23-hydroxylated bile acids, in scymnol, chimaerol and ranol, as well as that at C-25 in scymnol, chimaerol and bufol, ought to be soluble by measurement of optical activity at appropriate wavelengths. Optical rotatory dispersion measurements have as yet found no application to structural problems of bile steroids, probably because they have not been made.

REFERENCES

Anderson, I. G., Briggs, T. & Haslewood, G. A. D. (1964) *Biochem. J.*, **90**, 303.
Bhacca, N. S. & Williams, D. H. (1964) *Applications of NMR Spectroscopy in Organic Chemistry*. San Francisco *etc.*: Holden-Day.
Bush, I. E. (1952) *Biochem. J.*, **50**, 370.
Carey, J. B. Jr. & Bloch, H. S. (1954) *J. lab. clin. Med.*, **44**, 486.
Carpenter, F. H. & Hess, G. P. (1956) *J. Am. chem. Soc.*, **78**, 3351.
Cohen, S. L. & Oneson, I. B. (1953) *J. biol. Chem.*, **204**, 245.
Cook, R. P. (1958) (Ed.). *Cholesterol*. New York: Academic Press.
Cross (1960) *see* References to Chapter Two.
Cross, A. D. (1964) *Biochem. J.*, **90**, 308; 314.
Evans, D. D. & Shoppee, C. W. (1953) *J. chem. Soc.*, p. 540.
Fischmeister, I. (1960) *Ark. Kemi.*, **16**, 151.
Haslewood, G. A. D. (1954) *Biochem. J.*, **56**, 581.
Haslewood, G. A. D. (1964) *Biochem. J.*, **90**, 309.
Kritchevsky, D. & Kirk, M. R. (1952) *Arch. Biochem. Biophys.*, **35**, 346.
Sandberg, D. H., Sjövall, J., Sjövall, K. & Turner, D. A. (1965) *J. Lipid Res.*, **6**, 182.
Shoppee, C. W. (1949) *J. chem. Soc.*, p. 1671.
Sjövall, J. (1955) *Ark. Kemi*, **8**, 299.
Sjövall, J. (1964) *Methods of Biochemical Analysis*, **12**, 97.
Wootton, I. D. P. (1953) *Nature, Lond.*, **172**, 954.

CHAPTER FOUR

Biosynthesis

4.1 Biosynthesis of bile acids and alcohols

In all vertebrates examined so far, bile salts appear to be made from cholesterol in the liver. The direct evidence that they are made in the liver is that in the few species used experimentally an isolated perfused liver will continue to produce bile salts for a time, and if perfused with radioactive cholesterol will secrete radioactive bile salts. Moreover, bile salts have never been found to be produced by any other organ. In obstructive jaundice, however produced, bile salts increase in concentration in the blood and may appear in the urine.

At the time of writing it is too early to assess the experimental value of methods by which bile salts can be made *in vitro* from cholesterol by preparations of liver tissue (e.g. Mendelsohn & Mendelsohn, 1965; Mitropoulos & Myant, 1966). Published studies on the course of biosynthesis have hitherto had to depend chiefly on animals in which a bile fistula can be made and maintained. This method has the disadvantage that in experiments carried out for a long time non-physiological conditions are set up which may not necessarily reflect normal processes. Bile fistulae are, of course, frequently made in human patients and provide an opportunity for biochemical investigations.

By giving radioactive cholesterol to animals having a biliary fistula or by feeding experiments, it has been satisfactorily shown that cholesterol is converted into the characteristic bile salts in the following species (for references, see Haslewood, 1964): man, domestic dog, laboratory rabbit, guinea-pig, rat, and mouse, domestic pig, domestic fowl, boa constrictor, alligator, toad (*Bufo vulgaris japonicus*), frog (*Rana catesbiana*) and carp (*Cyprinus carpio*); in the last three species intact animals were used. It is therefore usually assumed that liver cholesterol (endogenous or exogenous) is converted to bile acids and alcohols in all vertebrates.

Cholesterol ((31); for formulae, see Fig. 4.1) is easily oxidized by molecular oxygen, and even non-enzymically at physiological pH and temperature, to the epimeric 7-hydroxycholesterols and 7α-hydroxycholesterol (32) is converted to cholic acid (2) in bile-fistula rats. The reaction (31)→(32), probably enzymically assisted (Danielsson & Einarsson, 1964; Mendelsohn, Mendelsohn & Staple, 1965), may be the first step in the process cholesterol→cholic acid in rats. Certainly no bile salt that is 'primary' (i.e. made by the liver directly from sterol) has been found that does not have a 7-hydroxyl group and, with the exception of β-muricholic (3α,6β,7β-trihydroxycholanic) acid of rat and mouse bile and ursodeoxycholic (3α,7β-dihydroxycholanic) acid, this group has the α-orientation.

The subsequent biosynthetic stages must include: (*a*) saturation of the C-5/C-6 double bond, (*b*) further hydroxylation at C-6, C-12, C-16 or C-23, (*c*) usually inversion of the hydroxyl group at C-3β to the C-3α configuration and (*d*) oxidation of the side chain.

In the formation of cholic acid (2) in mammals there is evidence that the stages (*a*), (*b*) and (*c*) occur before (*d*); i.e. the cholic acid nucleus is completely formed before the side chain is oxidized. Mendelsohn & Staple (1963) have described an enzymic system in rat liver capable of converting cholesterol to 3α,7α,12α-trihydroxy-5β-cholestane (36), a substance having the cholic acid nucleus and cholesterol side chain. This compound is an effective precursor of cholic acid in bile fistula rats; unlike 3β-hydroxy-5-cholenic acid, which has the cholesterol nucleus and the cholic acid side chain (Bergström *et al.*, 1960). Danielsson (1960) showed that 3α,7α,12α-trihydroxy-5β-cholestane (36) was oxidized by rat-liver homogenates and by washed rat-liver mitochondria to 3α,7α,12α,26-tetrahydroxy-5β-cholestane (37), i.e. these preparations brought about side-chain terminal oxidation. The tetrol (37) was oxidized by mouse-liver homogenates to 3α,7α,12α-trihydroxycoprostanic acid (21); the intermediate aldehyde, 3α,7α,12α-trihydroxy-5β-cholestane-26-al, was also converted to (21) by the mitochondrial, microsomal and soluble fractions of rat liver homogenates (Okuda & Danielsson, 1965).

3α,7α,12α-Trihydroxycoprostanic acid (21) is a very effective precursor of cholic acid in bile fistula rats, whatever the configuration at C-25 (Bergström *et al.*, 1960). It has been isolated from human fistula bile in small amounts (Carey & Haslewood, 1963). Human bile-fistula patients formed radioactive $3\alpha,7\alpha,12\alpha$-trihydroxycoprostanic acid when given ^{14}C-4- or ^{14}C-26-cholesterol intravenously (Staple & Rabinowitz, 1962) and when the isolated ^{14}C-4 acid was administered to another bile fistula patient radioactive cholic acid was obtained from the bile (Carey, 1964). Thus it seems very likely that (21) loses three carbon atoms to become cholic acid in the normal mammalian biosynthesis. Suld, Staple & Gurin (1962) have found evidence that these carbon atoms are removed as propionyl-CoA. Masui & Staple (1966) showed that $3\alpha,7\alpha,12\alpha,24\xi$-tetrahydroxycoprostanic acid (i.e. (21) with $^-$OH at C-24) was converted to cholic acid by rat-liver mitochondria + supernatant fractions; thus, varanic acid (Table 2.4) or one of its epimers at C-24 or C-25 may be an intermediate in cholic acid biosynthesis.

The way in which the nuclear changes are brought about is not fully understood, but H. Danielsson and his colleagues (see Danielsson, 1963, Berséus *et al.*, 1965 and Danielsson & Einarsson, 1966) have produced good evidence for the sequence $(32) \rightarrow (35)$ in rat liver (Fig. 4.1). 7α-Hydroxycholesterol (32) is dehydrogenated at C-3 and the double bond shifted to C_{4-5}, to give (33). This stage will require at least two enzymes; the dehydrogenase may be NAD-linked as in the case of similar enzymes well known in steroid biosynthesis; enzymes are also capable of catalysing the $C_{5-6} \rightarrow C_{4-5}$ shift of the double bond (see Talalay, 1965). (33) is probably the chief substrate for the 12α-hydroxylase enzyme system, and this then gives (34). Saturation of the double bond in (34) (by an NADPH-linked enzyme) gives the 5β-cholestane (coprostane) configuration in (35) and reduction at C-3 (NADH- or NADPH-linked) leads to $3\alpha,7\alpha,12\alpha$-trihydroxy-5β-cholestane (36). As mentioned above, this substance can be converted to the tetrol (37) and to trihydroxycoprostanic acid (21) by liver preparations from rats and mice and there is strong evidence for the conversion of trihydroxycoprostanic acid to cholic acid in rats and men.

The above sequence is given in Fig. 4.1.

The reactions shown in Fig. 4.1 can be modified to account for other bile acids and also bile alcohols. Thus, in the biogenesis of chenodeoxycholic ($3\alpha,7\alpha$-dihydroxycholanic) acid (formula, p. 55), a principal

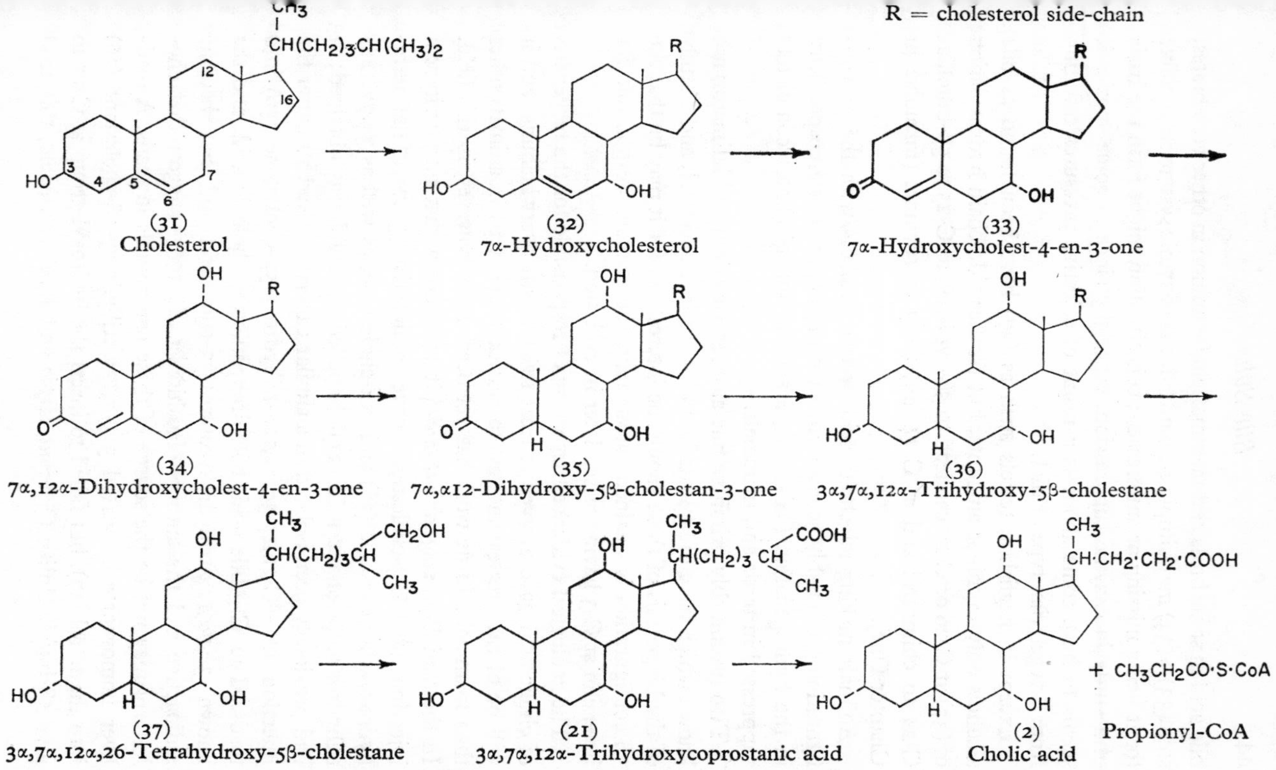

R = cholesterol side-chain

(31)
Cholesterol

(32)
7α-Hydroxycholesterol

(33)
7α-Hydroxycholest-4-en-3-one

(34)
7α,12α-Dihydroxycholest-4-en-3-one

(35)
7α,α12-Dihydroxy-5β-cholestan-3-one

(36)
3α,7α,12α-Trihydroxy-5β-cholestane

(37)
3α,7α,12α,26-Tetrahydroxy-5β-cholestane

(21)
3α,7α,12α-Trihydroxycoprostanic acid

(2)
Cholic acid

+ CH₃CH₂CO·S·CoA
Propionyl-CoA

Fig. 4.1 *Possible pathways for cholic acid biosynthesis in mammals.*

43

bile acid in some birds and mammals and common in other vertebrates, step (33)→(34) may simply be omitted, the enzymic system responsible for it being missing or suppressed; this situation might form the basis of a study in enzyme suppression, especially since in some species it seems to have come about as a result of selective pressures resulting from a vegetarian type of diet.

Except in hagfishes, tetrols such as (37) have been found as bile alcohols only in minor amounts, but further side-chain hydroxylation of (37) at C-26 or C-27 can lead to 5β-cyprinol, at C-25 to 5β-bufol, at C-24 to chimaerol and at C-24 and C-27 to scymnol (formulae in Chapter One).

Animals making allocholic acid or bile alcohols with the 5α-configuration presumably have enzymes with the opposite stereospecificity in the hydrogenation (34)→(35), a state of affairs almost completely suppressed in birds and mammals.

Two presumably primitive bile alcohols (myxinol and latimerol) are known which have the 3β configuration, as in cholesterol, and a study of the biogenesis of these should be interesting, for it may be that the 3β configuration is retained throughout, the enzymes responsible for inversion at C-3 having arisen later in evolution.

The zoological evidence that enzymes responsible for the biogenesis of cholic acid have evolved at least twice seems overwhelming, and it will be of the greatest interest to elucidate the steps in animals other than mammals. Little work has yet been done, however, in this field. In the toad *Bufo vulgaris japonicus* it was shown that intraperitoneal injection of ^{14}C-4-cholesterol gave radioactive 3α,7α,12α,26-tetrahydroxy-5β-cholestane (37) and -5α-cholestane, as well as 3α,7α,12α-trihydroxycoprostanic acid (21). Labelled 5β-bufol was obtained; it had previously been isolated in a similar experiment and also after the injection of [14]C-26,27-3α,7α,12α-trihydroxy-5β-cholestane (36) into toads. The C_{28} bile acid, trihydroxybufosterocholenic acid, and the known 3α,7α,12α-trihydroxycoprost-23-enic acid did not become radioactive and the authors (Hoshita *et al.*, 1965) suggest that cholesterol may not be the source of these compounds in toads. A toad-liver homogenate converted 3α,7α,12α-trihydroxy-5β-cholestane (36) into the tetrol (37), but failed to insert the hydroxyl group at C-25 to give 5β-bufol. Unlike *Cyprinus carpio* and *Rana catesbiana*, this toad could not, apparently, make cholic acid. The extent to which any of the toad bile salts may be artifacts caused by the intervention of micro-organisms or other parasites has not been explored further. Unless bile fistulae are made in animals or unless biosyntheses are accomplished *in vitro* or by germ-free specimens, there must be some doubt about the source of substances found in the bile. This is true not only for the toad but also the frog *Rana catesbiana* and the carp *Cyprinus carpio*. Carp fed for a year on a meat diet, containing little or no sterol except cholesterol, formed 5α-cyprinol 'normally' and those injected with ^{14}C-4-cholesterol gave the radioactive bile alcohol (Hoshita, 1964); nevertheless, the biosynthesis of the cyprinols or ranols has not yet been accomplished in conditions excluding microbial intervention.

Scymnol (3α,7α,12α,24ξ,26,27-hexahydroxy-5β-cholestane; see p. 19) was a poor precursor of cholic acid in bile fistula rats: yields of cholic acid from 5β-bufol (formula, p. 23) in these animals was also poor, but 5β-ranol (3α,7α,12α,24ξ,26-pentahydroxy-27-nor-5β-cho-lestane; see p. 23) was converted to cholic acid almost as efficiently as 3α,7α,12α-trihydroxy-5β-cholestane (36) itself (Danielsson & Kazuno, 1964).

The scheme shown in Fig. 4.1 is, of course, one based on the results of a number of discrete experiments, some with fistula animals and others with various preparations of liver tissue from more than one mammalian species. The result is a composite picture of a likely se-quence of biosynthetic events in mammalian liver and cannot at present be taken to represent certain knowledge of how cholesterol becomes cholic acid. The work done suggests indeed that other path-ways must be considered. In particular, it seems possible that 7α-hydroxycholesterol (32) might be converted to 7α,12α-dihydroxy-cholesterol (38) and thence to (34).

(38) 7α,12α-Dihydroxycholesterol

Danielsson (1961) showed that mouse-liver homogenates could convert (32) not only to (33) but also to another substance that was probably the 26-hydroxy derivative of (33); this was converted by bile fistula rats to both cholic and chenodeoxycholic acids. Danielsson (1962) found that 12α-hydroxycholesterol, tritium labelled, was quite efficiently converted into deoxycholic (3α,12α-dihydroxycholanic) acid in rabbits and radioactive cholic acid was also formed. Danielsson (1963) himself expresses the view that the biosynthetic pathway for chenodeoxycholic acid may be different from that for cholic acid; presumably the routes would diverge after the formation of 7α-hydroxycholesterol (32).

Björkhem & Danielsson (1965) made both epimers of 3-tritio-^{14}C-4-3,7α,12α-trihydroxycholest-4-ene (39) and found that both were efficiently converted to cholic acid in rats with a bile fistula. The ratio ^{3}H/^{14}C in the cholic acid formed suggested that a 3-keto steroid had been an intermediate. No conclusion was reached as to whether the double bond could, in the usual biosynthesis from cholesterol, migrate to C_{4-5} before oxidation to keto at C-3.

(39) 3-Tritio-^{14}C-4-3,7α,12α-trihydroxycholest-4-ene

It has been shown that in all probability chenodeoxycholic acid is the precursor of α-muricholic (3α,6β,7α-trihydroxycholanic) acid in rat and mouse bile and of hyocholic (3α,6α,7α-trihydroxycholanic) acid in pigs. Hence in rats and mice there must be active 6β-hydroxylating and in pigs 6α-hydroxylating enzymic systems (Bergström *et al.*, 1960). Such systems have been directly demonstrated in fractionated pig liver preparations, with lithocholic (3α-hydroxycholanic) acid as a substrate (Kurata, 1964).

β-Muricholic (3α,6β,7β-trihydroxycholanic) acid is probably made in rats from α-muricholic acid.

Ursodeoxycholic (3α,7β-dihydroxycholanic) and 3α-hydroxy-7-oxo-cholanic acids are certainly often secondary products, made in the intestine from chenodeoxycholic acid as described in Chapter Five. However, both these acids can be made also in rat and guinea-pig liver, the keto acid being an intermediate in the biogenesis of ursodeoxycholic acid.

It is not known whether phocaecholic (3α,7α,23ξ-trihydroxycholanic) acid is a primary bile acid in pinnipedia (seals, sea-lions and walruses), but if it is, then chenodeoxycholic acid seems a likely precursor.

Thus, it seems that cholic acid is a primary bile acid not itself metabolized further to any great extent in the liver, but giving rise to intestinal products which can themselves be further altered (Chapter Five). On the other hand, chenodeoxycholic acid by further hydroxylation (but not, apparently, at C-12) in the liver is the origin of several primary bile acids, some of which are major constituents of the bile salts of certain mammals.

Inversion of configuration at C-3 and hydroxylation at C-7 can be brought about by rats and rabbits even when a C_{5-6} double bond is not

(40) 3β-Hydroxy-5α-cholestane (cholestanol)

initially present. Thus, when ^{14}C-4-3β-hydroxy-5α-cholestane (40) was given intracardially to bile fistula rats, radioactive allocholic acid (formula (3), p. 7) was found in the bile (Karavolas *et al.*, 1965). A similar reaction was demonstrated in rabbits (Hofmann & Mosbach, 1964), which formed gallstones consisting chiefly of allodeoxycholic (3α,12α-di-hydroxyallocholanic) acids, presumably after intestinal micro-organisms had removed the ^-OH group at C-7α from allocholic acid (see Chapter Five).

The 5β-epimer of (40), 3β-hydroxy-5β-cholestane (coprostanol, coprosterol), was similarly converted to cholic, α- and β-muricholic, 3α,6β-dihydroxycholanic, chenodeoxycholic and lithocholic acids in rats (Bell *et al.*, 1965).

In spite of much effort, the subcellular mechanisms of bile acid formation remain largely unknown. One of the most investigated reactions is that of hydroxylation of the steroid nucleus (see, e.g., Talalay, 1965); nevertheless, the means by which it is brought about are by no means well understood. Molecular oxygen is thought by most investigators to be the ultimate source of the oxygen atom in OH, but the chemical species involved have not been identified. The enzymes concerned seem to be located partly in the microsomal fraction and for maximally efficient lithocholic acid hydroxylation, glutathione (GSH), NAD and Mg^{2+} are required, as well as co-factors present in boiled supernatant fraction (Kurata, 1964). Quite clearly, more general biochemical information is needed in this field before an attempt can be made to correlate the differences in hydroxylation pattern with diet or other selective factors which have led to such differences.

The enzymes responsible in rat and mouse liver for removal of propionic acid from the cholesterol side chain are undoubtedly mitochondrial and are stereospecific in their initial attack on C-26* (Berséus, 1965; Mitropoulos & Myant, 1965). As remarked above, however, both C-25 epimers of 3α,7α,12α-trihydroxycoprostanic acid (21) are efficient precursors of cholic acid in bile fistula rats. Herman & Staple (1965) have shown that the tetrol (37) can be oxidized to the trihydroxycoprostanic acid (21) by a $10^5 \times$ **g** supernatant from a rat-liver homogenate, requiring only NAD as co-factor.

4.2 Conjugation

It seems likely that the bile acids are converted into their CoA derivatives in the liver and that these are condensed with glycine or taurine to give the conjugates. The sequence may be, for taurine conjugates (Elliott, 1956):

---

* In numbering the carbon atoms of the terminal methyl groups in the cholesterol side chain, C-26 is regarded as the one derived by biosynthesis from the β-methyl group in mevalonic acid.

(i) $R \cdot COOH + CoA \cdot SH + ATP \longrightarrow$
   Cholic acid   CoA

                    $R \cdot CO \cdot S \cdot CoA + AMP + Pyrophosphate$
                    Cholyl CoA

(ii) $R \cdot CO \cdot S \cdot CoA + H_2N \cdot CH_2 \cdot CH_2 \cdot SO_3^- \longrightarrow$
                Taurate

                    $R \cdot CO \cdot NH \cdot CH_2 \cdot CH_2 \cdot SO_3^- + CoA \cdot SH$
                    Taurocholate

In rats glycine conjugates constitute about 5 per cent of the bile salts, but if the animals are given a diet deficient in cysteine, methionine or pyridoxine (a factor required for the formation of taurine) they conjugate a much greater proportion of their bile acids with glycine: adrenalectomy has a similar effect (references in Haslewood, 1964). Bremer (1956) showed that rat-liver microsomes would conjugate cholic and deoxycholic ($3\alpha,12\alpha$-dihydroxycholanic) acids with both glycine and taurine, whereas those from the liver of the domestic fowl and rabbit would conjugate with taurine and chiefly glycine respectively. Human-liver homogenates will make both glycine and taurine conjugates and the proportions of each may be altered in disease (Chapter Six).

According to Peric-Golia & Jones (1962), guinea-pig- and rat-liver homogenates will conjugate preferentially with L-ornithine and these authors suggest that in guinea-pigs this form of conjugation is a non-specific effect of hepatic injury.

Free bile acids have not been detected in more than very small amounts in fresh bile from any healthy animal, except toads, but may occur in disease or in response to various types of physiological or nutritional insult.

Some bile alcohols have been shown to form their conjugates when incubated with frog-liver homogenates and ^{35}S sulphate (Bridgwater & Ryan, 1957) and it may be supposed that the usual 'active sulphate' (phosphoadenosine phosphosulphate) is involved.

REFERENCES

Bell, R. G., Hsia, S. L., Matschiner, J. T., Doisy, E. A., Jr., Elliott, W. H., Thayer, S. A. & Doisy, E. A. (1965) *J. biol. Chem.*, **240**, 1054.

Bergström, S., Danielsson, H. & Samuelsson, B. (1960) In *Lipide Metabolism.* Ed. K. Bloch. pp. 291–336. New York: John Wiley & Sons.

Berséus, O. (1965) *Acta chem. scand.*, **19**, 325.

Berséus, O., Danielsson, H. & Kallner, A. (1965) *J. biol. Chem.*, **240**, 2396.

Björkhem, I. & Danielsson, H. (1965) *Acta chem. scand.*, **19**, 2298.

Bremer, J. (1956) *Biochem. J.*, **63**, 507.

Bridgwater, R. J. & Ryan, D. A. (1957) *Biochem. J.*, **65**, 24P.

Carey, J. B., Jr., (1964) *J. clin. Invest.*, **43**, 1443.

Carey, J. B., Jr., & Haslewood, G. A. D. (1963) *J. biol. Chem.*, **238**, PC 855.

Danielsson, H. (1960) *Acta chem. scand.*, **14**, 348.

Danielsson, H. (1961) *Ark. Kemi*, **17**, 363.

Danielsson, H. (1962) *Acta chem. scand.*, **16**, 1534.

Danielsson, H. (1963) In *Advances in Lipid Research*, Ed. R. Paoletti & D. Kritchevsky, Vol. 1, p. 335. New York: Academic Press.

Danielsson, H. & Einarsson, K. (1964) *Acta chem. scand.*, **18**, 831.

Danielsson, H. & Einarsson, K. (1966) *J. biol. Chem.*, **241**, 1449.

Danielsson, H. & Kazuno, T. (1964) *Acta chem. scand.*, **18**, 1157.

Elliott, W. H. (1956) *Biochem. J.*, **62**, 433.

Haslewood, G. A. D. (1964) *Biol. Rev.*, **39**, 537.

Herman, R. & Staple, E. (1965) *Fed. Proc.*, **24**, 661.

Hofmann & Mosbach (1964) *see* References to Table 2.1.

Hoshita, T. (1964) *Steroids*, **3**, 523.

Hoshita *et al.* (1965) *see* Reference [14] in Table 2.5.

Karavolas, H. J., Elliott, W. H., Hsia, S. L., Doisy, E. A., Jr., Matschiner, J. T., Thayer, S. A. & Doisy, E. A. (1965) *J. biol. Chem.*, **240**, 1568.

Kurata, Y. (1964) *J. Biochem., Tokyo*, **55**, 415.

Masui, T. & Staple, E. (1966) *J. biol. Chem.* **241**, 3889.

Mendelsohn, D. & Mendelsohn, L. (1965) *S. Afr. J. med. Sci.*, **30**, 42.

Mendelsohn, D., Mendelsohn, L. & Staple, E. (1965) *Biochim. Biophys. acta*, **97**, 379.

Mendelsohn, D. & Staple, E. (1963) *Biochemistry*, **2**, 577.

Mitropoulos, K. A. & Myant, N. B. (1965) *Biochem. J.*, **97**, 26C.

Mitropoulos, K. A. & Myant, N. B. (1966) *Biochem. J.*, **99**, 51P.

Okuda, K. & Danielsson, H. (1965) *Acta chem. scand.*, **19**, 2160.

Peric-Golia, L. & Jones, R. S. (1962) *Proc. Soc. exp. Biol. N.Y.*, **110**, 327.

Staple, E. & Rabinovitz, J. L. (1962) *Biochim. Biophys. acta*, **59**, 735.

Suld, H. M., Staple, E. & Gurin, S. (1962) *J. biol. Chem.*, **237**, 338.

Talalay, P. (1965) *Ann. Rev. Biochem.*, **34**, 347.

CHAPTER FIVE

Artifacts of the Enterohepatic Circulation

5.1 General consideration of artifacts

In some mammals evidence has been obtained suggesting that whereas fat absorption takes place to a large extent at the beginning of the jejunum, most of the bile salts are probably absorbed much lower down the intestinal tract, chiefly in the ileum (for diagram, see p. 2, and for references, Senior (1964)). This state of affairs implies that for a substantial time the bile salts will be exposed to the action of the numerous micro-organisms normally resident in the lower small intestine and perhaps also to those in the caecum. The effects of this exposure can be studied in several ways; for example by comparing the bile salts of animals that are 'germ-free' or infected with known micro-organisms with those of normal ('conventional') specimens, by comparing gall-bladder bile with fistula bile in the same species, by examination of intestinal or faecal bile salts and by incubation of bile salts with intestinal contents or isolated micro-organisms.

5.2. Germ-free organisms

It is not very difficult to raise and keep some vertebrates in the sterile condition and this is routinely done with domestic chicks, rats and mice. Other animals, for example *Rhesus* monkeys, rabbits, hamsters, guinea-pigs and turkeys have also been kept sterile, with varying degrees of success (Reyniers, 1959).

The faecal bile salts of germ-free rats are the same as those that can be collected from a biliary fistula, namely chiefly the taurine conjugates of cholic and chenodeoxycholic acids. Such rats have been infected with

51

known organisms and only limited changes noted in the faecal bile acids (Bergström *et al.*, 1960; Gustafsson & Norman, 1962).

Germ-free chick bile contains allocholic, cholic and chenodeoxycholic acids as taurine conjugates, but not the 3α-hydroxy-7-oxocholanic acid found in conventional fowl bile.

Although they are frequently not 'normal' in some ways (for instance, in rats and guinea-pigs the caecum is greatly enlarged), germ-free animals are carrying out their full physiological functions; hence investigations of characters usually affected by intestinal parasites are especially valuable in a context in which surgical interference or other insult is avoided.

5.3 Biliary fistulae

(For most of the references to this section the reader should consult the article by Bergström *et al.* (1960).)

Fistulae through which bile can be collected are fairly easily established and can be maintained for many days in some species. In animals without gall-bladders, e.g. rats, bile cannot usually be collected by any other method. If the fistula is maintained so as to exclude passage of bile to the intestine for a sufficiently long time it can be assumed that intestinal artifacts of bile salts will disappear; the bile will then contain only bile salts as produced by the liver, albeit in abnormal physiological circumstances. In such conditions the rabbit, which normally has almost exclusively glycine-conjugated deoxycholic ($3\alpha,12\alpha$-dihydroxycholanic) acid (formula (41)) as a bile salt, produces progressively more glycine-conjugated cholic acid, until, after some days, deoxycholic acid has entirely vanished.

(41) Deoxycholic acid

Rat fistula bile, on the contrary, contains no deoxycholic acid and when radioactive deoxycholic acid or its taurine conjugate are injected into this animal they are rapidly and quantitatively converted into radioactive taurocholate. It can therefore be assumed that this species, unlike the rabbit, has an effective 7α-hydroxylase liver enzyme system which does not allow intestinally-formed deoxycholic acid to accumulate in the bile; the same is true of the laboratory mouse.

In man no conversion of deoxycholic to cholic acid occurs, but deoxycholic acid disappears eventually from human fistula bile, provided that the intestinal part of the enterohepatic circulation is excluded.

In a python in which a biliary fistula was maintained it was found that pythocholic ($3\alpha,12\alpha,16\alpha$-trihydroxycholanic) acid was replaced by cholic acid, but was re-formed when deoxycholic acid was injected. The conclusion was that snakes of the family Boidae, which contain pythocholic acid, make this compound by 16α-hydroxylation in the liver of deoxycholic acid formed in the intestine from cholic acid.

In the examples quoted above, the cholic acid formed by the liver is a 'primary' bile acid, and deoxycholic and pythocholic acids are 'secondary' to this in the biles in which they occur. Of course, part of the cholic acid in rat and mouse bile is secondary also.

In rabbits fed 3β-hydroxy-5α-cholestane (cholestanol; formula, p. 47) there were found gallstones consisting largely of allodeoxycholic acid ($3\alpha,12\alpha$-dihydroxyallocholanic acid); presumably the rabbit makes allocholic acid from cholestanol and this, like cholic acid, is deoxygenated at C-7 by intestinal micro-organisms (Hofmann & Mosbach, 1964). Cholestanol itself can probably be formed by reduction of cholesterol by intestinal micro-organisms, but it can also be biosynthesized from mevalonate or made from cholesterol by homogenates of rat and guinea-pig liver (Shefer, Milch & Mosbach, 1965).

In pigs, fistula bile contains glycine and taurine conjugates of hyocholic and chenodeoxycholic acids only, hence the hyodeoxycholic, $3\alpha,6\beta$- and $3\beta,6\alpha$-dihydroxycholanic, 3α-hydroxy-6-oxocholanic and lithocholic acids present in the gall-bladder bile presumably arise by removal of the oxygen at C-7 in the primary bile acid in the intestine, followed by alterations at C-3 and C-6.

There must be in the vertebrate intestine micro-organisms which are very efficient at deoxygenation of bile salts or bile acids at C-7. It has

E

been shown, by the use of tritium-labelled cholic acid in rats with biliary fistulae, that the elimination of the 7α-OH group from cholic and hyocholic acids occurs by dehydration with the C-6β hydrogen atom, to give a C_{6-7} double bond, which is then hydrogenated by *trans* addition of 2H (Fig. 5.1).

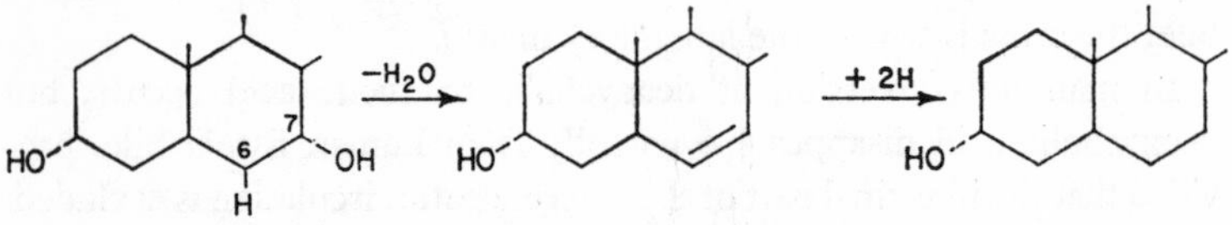

Fig. 5.1   *Formation of deoxycholic from cholic acid.*

5.4 *In vitro* coversion of cholic to deoxycholic acid

The removal of oxygen from cholic acid to give deoxycholic acid by incubation with mixtures of micro-organisms is a reaction frequently claimed in the older literature to have been demonstrated; these earlier claims were made uncertain by doubts concerning the purity of the cholic acid (made from ox bile, usually rich in deoxycholic acid) used as a substrate. However, the use of radioactive cholic acid has put the experimental basis of *in vitro* 7α-deoxygenation of this beyond reasonable doubt.

5.5 3α-Hydroxy-7-oxocholanic acid

There is no evidence that deoxycholic acid, which is common in mammalian biles, can ever be a primary bile acid made from cholesterol in the liver, but 3α-hydroxy-7-oxocholanic acid (formula (42)) can apparently be both primary and secondary.

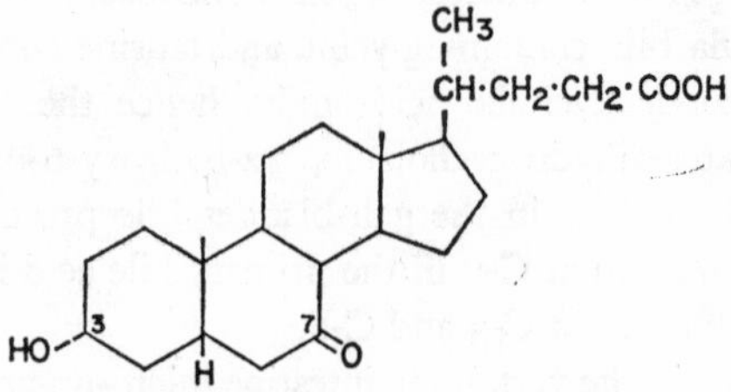

(42) 3α-Hydroxy-7-oxocholanic acid

3α-Hydroxy-7-oxocholanic acid is found in rat and guinea-pig bile; rat liver can reduce it to ursodeoxycholic (3α,7β-dihydroxycholanic) acid (partial formula (43)), whilst the guinea-pig makes chiefly chenodeoxycholic acid (44) from (42), although a little ursodeoxycholic acid is probably formed also (Danielsson & Einarsson, 1964) (Fig. 5.2).

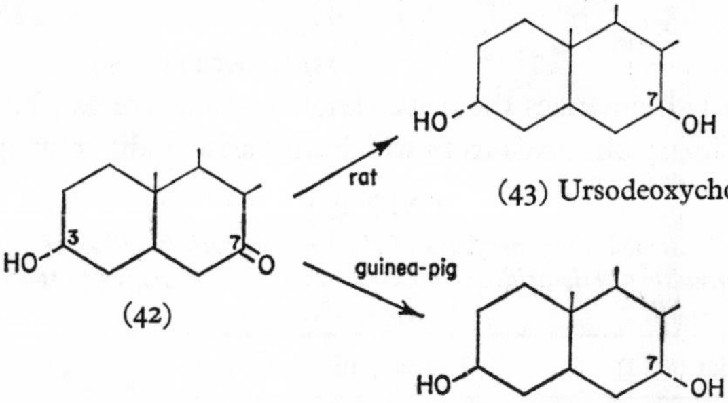

(42)

(43) Ursodeoxycholic acid

(44) Chenodeoxycholic acid

Fig. 5.2 *Chief reduction products of 3α-hydroxy-7-oxocholanic acid by liver of two species.*

According to Bergström *et al.* (1960), acid (42) is not made by guinea-pigs from cholesterol, but Peric-Golia & Jones (1961) said it could arise 'independently of enteric passage'; the point was conceded by Danielsson & Einarsson (1964), who, however, continue to disagree with Peric-Golia & Jones about the principal bile salts in this species.* 3α-Hydroxy-7-oxocholanic acid is a principal bile acid in some mammals, for example the coypu and koala, and it is not known whether it is primary or arises from chenodeoxycholic acid in these animals. Its absence from germ-free chick bile argues that in this bird it is a microbial artifact.

5.6 Other artifacts

Lithocholic (3α-hydroxycholanic) acid (45) is certainly a microbial product, made from chenodeoxycholic acid. It and its conjugates are too insoluble to function as effective bile salts, but may possibly be a cause of liver disease in man (see Chapter Six). From rat and human faeces there have been isolated single, not fully identified, strains of micro-organisms that could effect 7α-dehydroxylation of chenodeoxycholic acid (Gustafsson *et al.*, 1966).

* Peric-Golia & Jones say that in young guinea-pigs it is cholic acid; Danielsson & Einarsson maintain that it is chenodeoxycholic acid.

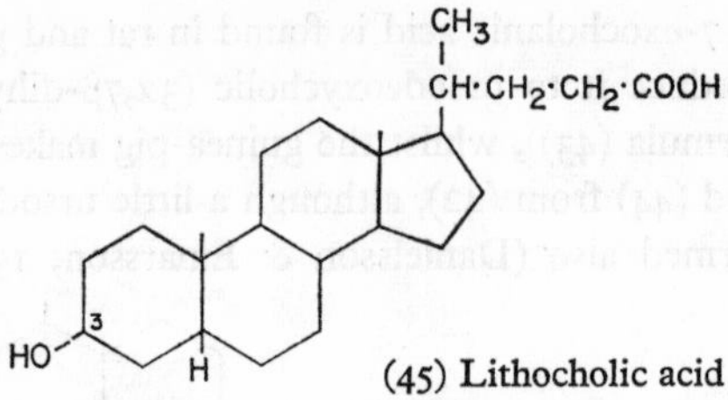

$$CH_3$$
$$CH \cdot CH_2 \cdot CH_2 \cdot COOH$$

HO   H

(45) Lithocholic acid

Table 5.1 summarizes the better-known artifacts of gall-bladder bile and the primary bile acids from which they arise in different species.

TABLE 5.1

Some biliary artifacts of the enterohepatic circulation
For formulae of bile acids see Chapter Two: for references to species, see Appendix.

Artifact (acid)	Primary bile acid	Species
? Bitocholic	$3\alpha,7\alpha,12\alpha,23\xi$-tetra-hydroxycholanic, or cholic→deoxycholic	Snakes of family Viperidae; other snakes
Pythocholic	Cholic→deoxycholic	Snakes of family Boidae
? $3\alpha,12\alpha$-Dihydroxy-7-oxocholanic	Cholic	Monkey; ox; python
? $7\alpha,12\alpha$-Dihydroxy-3-oxo- and 3α-hydroxy-7,12-dioxocholanic	Cholic	Ox
Deoxycholic	Cholic	Man; rabbit; ox and many other mammals; python
Hyodeoxycholic	Hyocholic	Pig; wart-hog
$3\alpha,6\beta$-Dihydroxy- and $3\beta,6\alpha$-dihydroxycholanic	Probably hyocholic→hyodeoxycholic	Pig
? Ursodeoxycholic	Chenodeoxycholic	Man; rat; coypu; bears
? 3α-Hydroxy-7-oxocholanic	Chenodeoxycholic	Coypu; guinea-pig; koala; domestic fowl
? 3α-Hydroxy-6-oxocholanic[a]	Probably hyocholic	Pig
? 3α-Hydroxy-12-oxocholanic	Probably cholic→deoxycholic	Ox
Lithocholic	Chenodeoxycholic	Man; pig; rabbit; guinea-pig[b]

? Indicates uncertainty about whether the acid, found in the bile, is always an intestinal artifact (see text).

[a] Isolated as the allo acid after alkaline hydrolysis of the bile salts.

[b] Danielsson & Einarsson (1964).

5.7 Biological significance of artifacts

The general significance of differences in bile salts in animal forms is discussed in Chapter Seven, and it may be noted here that the response of the host animal to intestinal artifacts seems to make sense in the light of our admittedly imperfect understanding of the functions of bile. The distribution of bile salts in eutherian (placental) mammals at least suggests that there is a strong correlation between bile-salt type and diet. Thus, carnivores and omnivores have taurine-conjugated tri-hydroxy bile acids, whilst herbivores (except bovids) tend to dihydroxy bile acids and glycine conjugates. The intervention of intestinal micro-organisms can apparently be fitted into this picture: thus, the rat and mouse (omnivorous) do not tolerate deoxycholic acid, but re-make cholic acid from it, whilst the rabbit and pig, presumably 'preferring' dihydroxy bile acids, obtain them through microbial action on cholic and hyocholic acids respectively.

The boid snakes that make pythocholic from deoxycholic acid do so presumably in response to 'unwanted' deoxycholic acid. Bitocholic acid in other snakes may be the result of a similar response (in this case, hydroxylation at C-23), and some snakes as well as other animals may re-hydroxylate deoxycholic acid at C-7α, as do the rat and mouse.

However, many mammals are apparently 'indifferent' to deoxycholic acid; these include carnivores such as the dog and omnivores like man, and it may be that in these cases the proportion of deoxycholic acid usually present is not sufficient, in the animal's circumstances, for its re-hydroxylation to offer enough selective advantage to ensure the survival of the liver enzymes responsible for it.

J. D. Smyth has drawn attention to the effect of bile salts on certain intestinal parasites, in particular *Echinococcus granulosus* the hydatid parasite of man and sheep. Eggs of this cestode parasite penetrate the intestinal mucosa in the intermediate host (for example, sheep, man) and form hydatid cysts, containing protoscolices of the parasite, in the liver and other organs. After the death of the intermediate host the cyst may be eaten by a definitive host (often a dog), in which completion of the life cycle takes place, the eggs of the parasite appearing in the faeces of the definitive host. This cycle is obviously open to the action of bile in both kinds of host. After keeping protoscolices of *E. granulosus* in axenic

58 *Bile Salts*

culture, Smyth has shown that these are very susceptible to deoxycholic acid and its conjugates, especially glycodeoxycholate, whilst unaffected by taurocholate. It may be that the presence of deoxycholate and other dihydroxy bile acid ions, and especially their glycine conjugates, offers some protection to certain mammals from parasites such as *E. granulosus*: similar arguments could perhaps be applied to other intestinal parasites, and in some cases bile salts like taurocholate might be essential to their development, although investigation in this field has hardly begun (Smyth & Haslewood, 1963).

REFERENCES

Bergström *et al.* (1960) *see* References to Chapter Four.
Gustafsson, B. E. & Norman, A. (1962) *Proc. Soc. exp. Biol. N.Y.*, **110**, 387.
Gustafsson, B. E., Midtvedt, T. & Norman, A. (1966) *J. exp. Med.* **123**, 413.
Danielsson, H. & Einarsson, K. (1964) *Acta chem. scand.*, **18**, 732.
Hofmann & Mosbach (1964) *see* References to Table 2.1.
Peric-Golia, L. & Jones, R. S. (1961) *Proc. Soc. exp. Biol., N.Y.*, **106**, 177.
Reyniers, J. A. (1959) *Ann. N.Y. Acad. Sci.*, **78**, 3.
Senior (1964) *see* References to Chapter One.
Shefer, S., Milch, S. & Mosbach, E. H. (1965) *J. Lipid Res.*, **6**, 33.
Smyth, J. D. & Haslewood, G. A. D. (1963), *Ann. N.Y. Acad. Sci.*, **113**.

CHAPTER SIX

Human Bile Salts

6.1 Composition of human bile

Table 6.1, compiled from various sources, shows the approximate composition of human gall-bladder and fistula bile.

TABLE 6.1

Approximate composition of human bile (g/100 ml)

Constituent	Hepatic (fistula) bile	Gall-bladder bile
Inorganic ions (total)		
(Na^+, K^+, Cl^-, HCO_3^-, Ca^{2+}, Fe^{2+}, etc.)	0·6–0·9	0·5–1·1
Fatty acids	0·1–0·14	0·9–1·6
Cholesterol (free)	0·004–0·21	0·01–1·3
Phospholipids, chiefly lecithin	0·1–0·6	1·0–5·8
Bile salts	0·7–1·4	1·0–9·2
Mucin, protein, bilirubin glucoronide, etc.	0·2–1·2	1·0–4·0
Alkaline phosphatases, (amylase), ? other enzymes		

By absorbing sodium and chloride ions and water in isotonic proportions, the gall-bladder has a concentrating effect.

The bile does not contain more than traces of esters either of cholesterol or of fatty acids, except, of course, for phosphatidyl choline (lecithin), which is a component whose significance for the solubilization of cholesterol and other fats has been rather neglected until recent times. Lecithins comprise most of the phospholipid in human bile; an example of such a compound is L-α-palmitoyl, β-oleoyl phosphatidyl choline (47).

Lecithins are primarily more important than the bile salts in holding

$$\text{CH}_3(\text{CH}_2)_7\cdot\text{CH}=\text{CH}\cdot(\text{CH}_2)_7\cdot\text{CO}\cdot\text{O}\cdot\overset{\displaystyle a\,\text{CH}_2\cdot\text{O}\cdot\text{CO}\cdot(\text{CH}_2)_{14}\text{CH}_3}{\underset{a'\text{CH}_2\cdot\text{O}\cdot\overset{\text{O}^-}{\underset{\overset{\|}{\text{O}}}{\text{P}}}\cdot\text{O}\cdot\text{CH}_2\cdot\text{CH}_2\cdot\overset{+}{\text{N}}(\text{CH}_3)_3}{\text{CH}\beta}}$$

(47) L-α-Palmitoyl, β-oleoyl phosphatidyl choline (a lecithin of human bile)

cholesterol in solution in human bile, and when they reach the intestine and are there converted into lysolecithins, for example by
removal of the oleoyl group by hydrolysis catalysed by pancreatic
phospholipase A, there are formed detergent substances of high potency
for the solubilization of fats (for a discussion, see Barton & Glover,
1965, Desai *et al.*, 1965 and Norman, 1965).

The pH of gall-bladder bile is rather less than that of fistula bile;
values of pH 7·5 and 8·0 respectively have been quoted for man
(Burnett, 1965).

6.2 Bile salts in bile

The primary bile acids in human bile are cholic and chenodeoxycholic
and these are the only ones, except for traces of allocholic acid and
3α,7α,12α-trihydroxycoprostanic acid, present in fistula bile provided
that the intestine is entirely excluded from the hepatic circulation.
Normally, however, deoxycholic acid and small amounts of lithocholic
acid as well as ursodeoxycholic (3α,7β-dihydroxycholanic) acid and keto
acids may occur, all formed after the action of intestinal micro-
organisms on the primary bile acids (Chapter Five). Of the secondary
acids, deoxycholic (formula, p. 52) is physiologically the most important, and may amount to 20 per cent by weight of the bile acids.

No more than traces of free bile acids are found in the bile and both
glycine and taurine conjugates occur, so that there are normally six
principal bile salts present, namely:

Primary bile salts	Glycocholate
	Taurocholate
	Glycochenodeoxycholate
	Taurochenodeoxycholate
Secondary bile salts	Glycodeoxycholate
	Taurodeoxycholate

At biliary pH (say 7·5–8·0) the taurine conjugates are as ions, $R \cdot CO \cdot NH \cdot CH_2 \cdot CH_2 \cdot SO_3^-$, and the glycine conjugates as ions, $R \cdot CO \cdot NH \cdot CH_2 \cdot COO^-$, with minor amounts of acids, $R \cdot CO \cdot NH \cdot CH_2 \cdot COOH$. The principal cations are Na^+ and K^+, with Na^+ predominant.

The glycine/taurine (G/T) ratio is variable, as is also the ratio trihydroxy/dihydroxy (T/D) bile acids. Figures given by Burnett (1965) are shown in Table 6.2.

TABLE 6.2

Glycine/taurine (G/T) and trihydroxy/dihydroxy (T/D) bile acid ratios in normal human bile (after Burnett, 1965)

Ratios (Mean $\pm$ S.E.)	Hepatic bile (no. of cases)	Gall-bladder bile (no. of cases)
G/T	2·2 $\pm$ 0·2 (10)	2·0 $\pm$ 0·2 (24)
T/D	1·2 $\pm$ 0·1 (10)	1·04 $\pm$ 0·08 (24)

The same author has found evidence that G/T may be slightly and T/D markedly lowered in patients with gallstones; G/T may be increased in hypothyroidism. Feeding healthy persons with taurine can increase the taurine conjugates, but glycine has no effect (Bergström *et al.*, 1960). The ratio cholic/chenodeoxycholic acids may be lowered slightly in hyperthyroid patients (Bergström & Danielsson, 1965). Liver biopsies from patients with liver disease show an ability to conjugate cholic acid with glycine that decreases with the duration of the disease (Ekdahl, 1958).

The human infant begins bile salt secretion as a taurine conjugator

TABLE 6.3

Average glycine/taurine (G/T) and trihydroxy/dihydroxy (T/D) bile acid ratios in human infants (after Poley et al., 1964). N.B. Except for the foetuses, bile was obtained from duodenal contents.

		Age (and number) of children				
Ratios	Foetuses(3) (22, 26 and 28 weeks)	2–24 hours (16)	2–5 days (8)	10 days– 7 months (8)	12 months– 3 years (6)	4–14 years (10)
G/T	0·09	0·2	0·5	1·9	2·7	1·3
T/D	1·0	1·5	2·2	2·0	1·8	0·7

almost entirely; glycine conjugates make their appearance gradually and are not present in 'adult' amounts for several months (Table 6.3). The T/D ratio is high in young children, but declines; presumably becoming stable in a range such as that given in Table 6.2. Poley *et al.* (1964) found that by the second half of gestation (which normally lasts 40 weeks in man) bile containing both glycine and taurine conjugates was present in foetal gall-bladders: the youngest foetus in their study was 22 weeks old. The infant bile studied (Table 6.3) was obtained from samples of duodenal contents collected by stomach tube, and it contained minor amounts of unidentified substances behaving on chromatograms like bile acid conjugates. Deoxycholic acid was not found in children younger than one year; presumably the micro-organisms responsible for its formation from cholic acid had not become sufficiently established to cause this change to a detectable extent.

It has been estimated that in an adult man about 0·8 g of bile acids are synthesized from cholesterol in 24 hours and that the circulating 'pool' of bile salts is about 3–5 g (Bergström *et al.*, 1960).

6.3 Bile salts in normal human blood

The most obvious reason for wishing to know the concentration of bile salts in blood is that it might be raised in obstructive jaundice and liver disease, and so its measurement might be of clinical value. These hopes have led to the development of a number of methods for estimating blood bile acid levels, with extremely variable results. Carey (1958) gives a list of reported values for cholic acid concentrations (mg/100 ml) in normal human blood serum ranging from 0 to 12; for dihydroxycholanic acids the range is from 0 to 52 mg/100 ml. Quite clearly, many (if not most) of the methods described up to 1958 are grossly inaccurate.

Carey (1958) himself elaborated a spectrophotometric method of measuring (*a*) cholic and (*b*) total dihydroxycholanic acids after alkaline hydrolysis of a partially purified protein-free extract of blood serum (3 ml). The bile acids were recovered by ether extraction of the acidified products of hydrolysis and were estimated by measurement of the colour produced after heating with 65 per cent (v/v) sulphuric acid at 60°. Measurements were made at from 220 to 410 mμ to include the absorption peaks given by pure cholic and chenodeoxycholic acids at 320 and 380 mμ respectively. In the conditions used by Carey, the absorption peak given by deoxycholic acid is at 385 mμ; by using chenodeoxycholic acid (absorption max at 380 mμ) as standard only a small error is introduced, and it is generally conceded that his method gives a reasonably reliable estimate of total trihydroxy- and dihydroxy-cholanic acids in human blood serum.

Carey gave values of 0–0·34 and 0–0·19 mg/100 ml for trihydroxy- and dihydroxycholanic acids respectively in human serum from 30 healthy persons (half of whom were women) aged 22–76 years. (For some reason, many analysts of serum bile acids quote their results as μg/ml, instead of μg/100 ml or mg/100 ml, as is more usual with blood constituents: Carey's figures are 0–3·4, etc., in μg/ml.)

The most reliable of the later spectrophotometric or fluorimetric methods are probably those in which the bile acids, after hydrolysis, are separated on paper chromatograms as described in Chapter Three, and after elution are estimated by measurement of the colour or fluorescence given with sulphuric acid. Errors can be readily incurred as a result of the elution of impurities from the paper, and for some of these methods, also, the results reported are undoubtedly too high. Osborn *et al.* (1959), using such a (fluorimetric) method, say that the 'total amount of bile acids in normal serum cannot be more than 1 or 2 mg per 100 ml'.

More recently, gas–liquid chromatography (GLC) has been used for this difficult analysis. In the method of Sandberg *et al.* (1965) the most satisfactory measurements were given by GLC with the fluorosilicone 'QF-1' as stationary phase and with the bile acids as the trifluoroacetates of their methyl esters. The bile salts were extracted from serum (5–10 ml) with an anion exchange resin and were then eluted from this with ethanolic ammonium carbonate. The eluate was evaporated, the residue was hydrolysed with alkali, and the bile acids extracted from the acidified product with ether. Methylation with diazomethane was followed by purification on an alumina column and, finally, the eluted methyl esters were treated with trifluoroacetic acid anhydride before GLC. The principal human bile acids could be separated, and the values given for 15 healthy persons (5 of whom were women) for serum cholic, chenodeoxycholic and deoxycholic acids were 0·002–0·065, 0·005–0·130 and 0·006–0·045 mg/100 ml respectively, in fair agreement with Carey's figures. Sandberg *et al.* give 0·03–0·23 mg/100 ml for total serum bile acids in fasting subjects, and in two other cases the levels rose from 0·04–0·06 to 0·18–0·32 mg/100 ml after a meal. Free (uncon-jugated) bile acids, in small proportions, were detected in normal sera.

6.4 Blood bile acids in disease

All observers are agreed that in liver disease and obstructive jaundice the blood concentrations are raised, often to many times the normal values. Sandberg *et al.* (1965) give levels between 0·39 and 20·1 mg/100 ml for total serum bile acids in patients with liver disease and say that in these cases there was little or no deoxycholic acid. In two such patients, between 3 and 5 per cent of the bile acids were unconjugated.

Carey (1958) and others attach little importance to the trihydroxy-dihydroxy (T/D) ratio in the serum in healthy people (Table 6.2), partly because of the analytical difficulties, but they regard a T/D ratio below about 1·0 as a poor prognostic sign in liver disease. However, Osborn *et al.* (1959) cite five patients with cirrhosis who had survived for a year after showing a T/D ratio of 0·5 or less.

An unpleasant feature of jaundice is frequently pruritus (itching), and this can be severe and prolonged in chronic disease of the liver or biliary tract. For many years argument has continued as to whether the pruritus is due to the increased concentration of blood bile salts. The itching can be sometimes relieved by giving steroid hormone analogues without lowering of the serum bile salts (e.g. see Osborn *et al.*, 1959), and this result is cited to support the view that the bile salts are not the proximate cause of the pruritus. However, a strongly basic polystyrene anion exchange resin ('cholestyramine') has been found to 'sequester' the intestinal bile salts, which are thus prevented from re-entering the enterohepatic circulation, and so are excreted with the faeces. This process would be expected to lower the serum bile acids, and Carey & Williams (1961) found that, in four patients with jaundice and pruritus, feeding cholestyramine did indeed lower the serum bile acid concentra-tions, finally to approximately normal values, and relieve the pruritus in every case. In two of the patients, one with biliary cirrhosis and another with metastic liver carcinoma, it was found that withholding the resin would cause the serum bile acid levels to rise and the pruritus to return; re-administration of the resin again lowered the bile acids and relieved the itching; the sequence was repeated also for a third time. A patient with obstruction (little or no bile reaching the duodenum) experienced neither relief nor lowering of serum bile acids after administration of the resin.

In 22 healthy pregnant women, Sjövall & Sjövall (1966) found, by GLC, a mean total serum bile acid concentration of 0·087 mg/100 ml and a mean T/D ratio of 0·5. In 6 cases (one jaundiced) of pruritus of late pregnancy the corresponding figures were 2·48 mg/100 ml and 4·1; after delivery, serum bile acid levels fell and pruritus disappeared.

These results and those reported by others (e.g. Van Itallie *et al.* 1961) point to a strong association between serum bile salt concentrations and the pruritus of jaundice, although there may be a time lag between the changes in serum levels and the onset or disappearance of symptoms. Any pathological mechanism by which bile salts could cause these results is at present purely speculative.

6.5 Lithocholic acid

Lithocholic (3α-hydroxycholanic, formula, p. 56) acid is a secondary bile acid, made by intestinal micro-organisms by removal of the hydroxyl group at C-7 from chenodeoxycholic acid (formula, p. 55). Strains of micro-organisms (not fully identified) from human and rat faeces have been found capable of this dehydroxylation (Gustafsson *et al.*, 1966). As its name implies, it and its salts are sparingly soluble, and until recently the acid was not considered likely to be absorbed in quantities sufficient to have any clinical effect. However, Holsti (1960) demonstrated that lithocholic acid introduced into rabbits' stomachs would induce cirrhosis of the liver, and Palmer *et al.* (1962) showed that this substance had potent pyrogenic and inflammatory activity in human subjects. It is present in human blood (Carey & Williams, 1965), bile and faeces, and there have been a number of studies of its metabolism in man. Carey & Williams (1963) found that two patients with complete biliary fistulae who were given [14]C-24-lithocholic acid intravenously excreted bile in which more than 90 per cent of the radioactivity was in conjugates of lithocholic acid: 2–3 per cent was in other forms, suggesting that the liver could transform lithocholic acid to a small extent. Norman & Palmer (1964) found that when [14]C-24-lithocholic acid was given orally to patients who, later, had their gall-bladders removed, radioactivity was present both in the faeces and gall-bladder bile. The faeces contained radioactive lithocholic acid, 3-oxocholanic acid and isolithocholic (3β-hydroxycholanic) acid, as well as an unidentified acid that could be hydrogenated to give cholanic acid itself. This unidentified acid was found in the bile, together with lithocholic and isolithocholic acids. Most of the faecal bile acid was unconjugated and although conjugation in the bile was complete or almost so, more than half the radioactive material was combined with substances other than glycine or taurine.

These interesting results do not themselves answer the question: can lithocholic acid be a cause of disease in man? However, they do provide biochemical information perhaps necessary to formulate a reply.

In rats, administration of lithocholic acid leads to bile duct hyperplasia and also to gallstones (Palmer & Hruban, 1966) containing substantial amounts of the 6β- and 7α-hydroxy derivatives (3α,6β-dihydroxycholanic and chenodeoxycholic acids) of lithocholic acid (Carey *et al.*, 1965); in contrast, the human liver does not hydroxylate this acid to any great extent.

6.6 Bile salts in urine

Bile salts have not been isolated from normal human urine but, traditionally, it is believed that it is the urinary bile salts in obstructive jaundice which have a surface tension-lowering effect sufficient to cause a positive response to Hay's test ('flowers of sulphur' sink when sprinkled on to the surface of the urine). This view rests on very shaky foundations. The response to Hay's test is capricious and bears no clear relation to the concentration of urinary bile pigment, although a relationship between bile-pigment and bile-salt concentrations is obvious in the blood plasma in obstructive jaundice. With normal urines the amount of bile salts that must be added to cause a positive Hay's test is such as to suggest that chemical identification would be easy, yet no reliable report has appeared of the isolation of bile salts from human urine in obstructive jaundice. Whilst it can hardly be doubted that bile salts are excreted by the kidney in increased amounts in such cases, there is no certainty that the concentration is sufficient to account for the response to Hay's test. Finally, the traditional view has probably hindered the examination of other potentially surface-tension-lowering compounds in human urine and the whole matter is one for re-investigation.

6.7 Bile acids in human faeces

The excretion of bile acids and of cholesterol itself into the bile constitute the only effective means by which cholesterol can be lost from the body. In spite of conflicting evidence, there is a strong belief that high levels of blood cholesterol predispose to atheromatous disease and, conversely, that it is desirable to maintain as low a blood cholesterol concentration as possible.

Analysis of the faeces should give values for the amount actually lost of both cholesterol and bile acids, but the picture is complicated by the considerable chemical changes brought about by intestinal micro-organisms. Cholesterol is reduced to coprosterol (3β-hydroxy-5β-cholestane) and otherwise altered, and the bile acids are converted to many substances, some of which are still unidentified and others are listed in Table 2.2, p. 11. Several methods for estimating these substances have been proposed and Grundy *et al.* (1965) have put forward a method for total faecal bile acid analysis by GLC, after column (fluorisil) and thin-layer chromatographic purification. They administered [14]C-24-cholic and -chenodeoxycholic acids to a patient and could recover 98 per cent of the radioactivity in their 'bile acid' fraction of the faecal extracts over a period of 38 days: the remaining 2 per cent was found in the urine. 50 μg of mixed bile acids was sufficient for analysis. The daily output of faecal bile acids in six patients with raised blood cholesterol and on a controlled diet ranged from 120 to 225 mg. The same group have also similarly measured the total faecal sterols (Miettinen *et al.*, 1965).

Danielsson (1963), in reviewing this subject, remarks that 'the main pathway for elimination of bile acids is excretion with feces and the rate of excretion should represent the rate of synthesis, yet measurements of bile acid production by determination of the half-life time and pool of bile acids yield values that are higher than those obtained for fecal excretion of bile acids'. The discrepancy remains unexplained.

The duodenum and upper part of the human small intestine usually contain a rather sparse microbial population, but this increases downwards until in the lower ileum and large bowel there are sufficient organisms to bring about profound chemical changes.

As will be obvious from what has been said above, most of the faecal bile acids are unconjugated and since there are no known endogenous

enzymes in animal tissue capable of splitting taurine or glycine conjugates, there must be intestinal micro-organisms that do have this
ability. Which organisms usually de-conjugate the bile salts *in vivo* is
not known, but a number of isolated species have been shown to be able
to split both types of conjugates *in vitro*: amongst these are strains of
Clostridium perfringens (Gustafsson *et al.*, 1957), some of which have
yielded cell-free extracts with this hydrolytic ability (Nair *et al.*, 1965).
15 strains of *Bacteroides* (*Fusiformis*) species from human saliva, jejunal
juice and faeces could split taurine and glycine conjugates of cholic
and deoxycholic acids (Drasar *et al.*, 1966). Further work on these
bacteria should result in preparations valuable to those interested in
bile acid analysis, as well as throwing light on a process important in
human cholesterol balance.

Several strains of bacteria have been shown to cause chemical changes
in the cholic acid nucleus (e.g. Hayakawa *et al.*, 1958), but the alterations
leading to some of the human faecal bile acids listed in Table 2.2, p. 11,
must have involved more than one enzymic reaction, and probably more
than one microbial species. The problem of identification of the
responsible organisms *in vivo* in man is a formidable one.

6.6 The gallstone problem

The many theories about gallstone formation have been reviewed by
Rains (1964). Infection and primary precipitation of bile pigments or
cholesterol have all been held to be principal causes of the stones. The
outstanding fact is that man is very much more prone to gallstones than
any other species. Even in domestic animals these are rare: in pigs they
consist chiefly of the calcium salts of lithocholic and $3\beta,6\alpha$-dihydroxy-
cholanic acids and in cattle of bile pigments. Human gallstones most
frequently contain a high proportion of cholesterol, although bile pigments are also usually present and sometimes predominate. The
inference is that man is often faced with the problem of excreting more
cholesterol (and perhaps also more of the breakdown products of
haemoglobin, i.e. bile pigments) than his physiological mechanisms can
manage. One way of assessing this situation is to conclude that it is a
result of failure of adaptation, in an evolutionary sense. The pastoral
phase of human history is very recent and the ancestors of *Homo sapiens*
acquired the ability to hunt with tools and other artifacts, and so to

capture cholesterol- and haemoglobin-rich food, probably not more than 1–3 million years ago (Cole, 1964), a short period on a geological time-scale. Before this, the ancestral human stock probably had a mainly vegetarian diet supplemented with such small animals as could be caught. A diet of this kind in living placental mammals (including the primates other than man) usually goes with bile salts, like those of man, having a good proportion of dihydroxy bile acids and (often) of glycine conjugates; in contrast, true carnivores have mainly cholic acid and taurine conjugates. Thus, man is to a great extent eating like a carnivore with the bile salts of an omnivore or herbivore; the relevant dietary difference is the very much greater amount of cholesterol with which the carnivore has to deal. If these arguments are sound, completely vegetarian people ('vegans') ought not to be liable to cholesterol gallstones; unfortunately there seems to be no reliable information on this point.

It is also arguable that there might be detectable deviations from normal in the bile of those having gallstones and this possibility has been explored. In a review, Juniper (1965) suggests that 'altered composition of the various bile salts may be important . . . in forming gallstones', whilst Burnett (1965) found that patients who had formed gallstones had a 'potentially lithogenic hepatic bile' showing one or more of the following features: a low total bile acid concentration, a low glycine/taurine ratio, a low trihydroxy/dihydroxy bile acid ratio. There was also sometimes a low lecithin concentration and an increased content of cholesterol. Phospholipids apparently play a very important part in solubilizing biliary cholesterol and lecithins may indeed be more significant than bile salts in this respect.

Schoenfield *et al.* (1966) analysed the bile salts in gallstones, finding up to 1 per cent (w/w) of these. Free bile acids (about 2 per cent of the total) were detected by GLC. The cores of stones contained relatively less conjugated deoxycholic acid and less taurine conjugates than the rest. After hydrolysis of isolated bile salts, GLC showed the presence of cholic, chenodeoxycholic, and deoxycholic acids, with small amounts of ursodeoxycholic, lithocholic, 3α-hydroxy-7-oxocholanic, and 3α-hydroxy-12-oxocholanic acids. The keto acids were also detected, for the first time, in human bile.

F

6.7 Enteroliths

Occasionally, and so far always in elderly women, bile acid stones are found in the small intestine. They appear to be associated with diverticulosis and some degree of stasis, and have an insoluble dietary residue as a nucleus. Chemical examination (Fowweather, 1949) has shown in all cases that the stones consisted chiefly of 'choleic acids', i.e. complexes of deoxycholic acid and fatty acid in a molecular ratio of (usually) 8 : 1. A little cholic acid was also present. A recent analysis of an enterolith apparently formed round an undigested vegetable stalk showed that, apart from this stalk, the material was almost all acidic, being about 23 per cent by weight fatty acids and the rest free (unconjugated) bile acid, mainly deoxycholic with a little cholic and chenodeoxycholic acids. The isolated choleic acid had oleic acid as the chief fatty acid in the complex (Bewes *et al.*, 1966).

A quite different stone was found in a man of 52 who had had a gastrojejunostomy since the age of 4. The afferent duodenojejunal loop so formed contained a concretion weighing (dry) 60 g, which consisted chiefly of cholic with smaller amounts of chenodeoxycholic acids (Fisher *et al.*, 1965).

It seems likely that bile acid enteroliths arise as a result of: (1) stasis, (2) accumulation of bile salts, (3) hydrolysis of conjugates by intestinal micro-organisms and (4) precipitation of water-insoluble acids at the pH prevailing.

REFERENCES

Barton, P. G. & Glover, J. (1965), Bergström, S. & Danielsson, H. (1965), Burnett, W. (1965), Desai, J. C., Glove, J. & Joo, C. N. (1965) and Norman, A. (1965) refer to articles in *The Biliary System*, Ed. W. Taylor, Oxford: Blackwell.

Bergström *et al.* (1960) *see* References to Chapter Four.

Bewes, P. C., Haslewood, G. A. D. & Roxburgh, R. A. (1966) *Brit. J. Surg.*, **53**, 709.

Carey, J. B. Jr., (1958) *J. clin. Invest*, **37**, 1494.

Carey, J. B. Jr., & Williams, G. (1961) *J. Am. med. Ass.*, **176**, 432.

Carey, J. B., Jr. & Williams, G. (1963) *J. clin. Invest*, **42**, 450.

Carey, J. B., Jr. & Williams, G. (1965) *Science*, **150**, 620.

Carey, J. B., Jr., Hoffbauer, F. W., Zaki, F. G. & Nwokolo, C. (1965) *Gastroenterology*, **48**, 809.

Cole, S. (1964). *The Prehistory of East Africa*. London: Weidenfeld & Nicolson.

Danielsson (1963) *see* References to Chapter Four.

Drasar, B. S., Hill, M. J. & Shiner, M. (1966) *Lancet* (i), 1237.

Ekdahl, Per-H. (1958) *Acta chir. scand.*, 115, 208.

Fisher, J. C., Bernstein, E. F. & Carey, J. B., Jr., (1965) *Gastroenterology*, 49, 272.

Fowweather, F. S. (1949) *Biochem. J.*, 44, 607.

Gustafsson, B. E., Bergström, S., Lindstedt, S. & Norman, A. (1957) *Proc. Soc. exp. Biol. N.Y.*, 94, 467.

Gustafsson *et al.* (1966) *see* References to Chapter Five.

Grundy, S. M., Ahrens, E. H., Jr., & Miettinen, T. A. (1965) *J. Lipid Res.*, 6, 397.

Hayakawa, S., Saburi, Y., Tamaki, K. & Hoshijima, H. (1958) *Nature*, Lond., 181, 906.

Holsti, P. (1960) *Nature*, Lond., 186, 250.

Juniper, K., Jr., (1965) *Am. J. Med.*, 39, 98.

Miettinen, T. A., Ahrens, E. H., Jr., & Grundy, S. M. (1965) *J. Lipid Res.*, 6, 411.

Nair, P. P., Gordon, M., Gordon, S., Reback, J. & Mendeloff, A. I. (1965) *Life Sciences*, 4, 1887.

Norman, A. & Palmer, R. H. (1964). *J. Lab. clin. Med.*, 63, 986.

Osborn, E. C., Wootton, I. D. P., da Silva, L. C. & Sherlock, S. (1959) *Lancet* (ii), 1049.

Palmer, R. H., Glickman, P. B. & Kappas, A. (1962) *J. clin. Invest.*, 41, 1573.

Palmer, R. H. & Hruban, Z. (1966) *J. clin. Invest*, 45, 1255.

Poley, J. R., Dower, J. C., Owen, C. A., Jr., & Stickler, G. B. (1964) *J. Lab. clin. Med.*, 63, 838.

Rains, A. J. Harding (1964) *Gallstones*. London: William Heinemann.

Sandberg *et al.* (1965) *see* References to Chapter Three.

Schoenfield, L. J., Sjövall J. & Sjövall, K. (1966) *J. Lab. clin. Med.*, 68, 186.

Sjövall, J. & Sjövall, K. (1966) *Clinica Chim. Acta*, 13, 207.

Van Itallie, T. B., Hashim, S. A., Crampton, R. S. & Tennent, D. M. (1961) *New Eng. J. Med.*, 265, 469.

CHAPTER SEVEN

Evolutionary Implications of Bile Salt Differences

7.1 The general picture

The bile salts listed in the Appendix show a close correlation between chemical types and systematic classification that can be readily understood in terms of evolutionary change. In steroid bile salts there is a progression from substances containing the entire C_{27} skeleton of cholesterol to C_{24} bile acids, and also from C_{27} (and C_{26}) bile alcohols conjugated with sulphate to C_{27} acids as taurine conjugates and then to C_{24} acids, finally conjugated with both glycine and taurine. In summary, the evolutionary course has evidently been: C_{27} (and C_{26}) alcohols (sulphates)$\rightarrow$$C_{27}$ acids (taurine conjugates)$\rightarrow$$C_{24}$ acids (taurine conjugates)$\rightarrow$$C_{24}$ acids (glycine conjugates). There is no evidence that C_{26} alcohols can re-form C_{27} compounds.

In this summary each chemical stage can be regarded as more advanced, in an evolutionary sense, than those previous to it; however, more than one stage may be represented at the same time in a single species.

There are also bile salts apparently confined within vertebrate groups but which do not seem to be more or less advanced in the sense discussed above.

It will be convenient to consider more closely the variations in bile salts in different animals by recognized groups: in the following account the reader should refer to the Appendix and, for formulae, to Chapter Two.

7.2 Invertebrates

Invertebrates do not have a distinct liver or bile, but in many cases the digestive fluids contain substances with detergent properties (Vonk, 1962). In the two crustaceans listed these substances have been found not to be steroids and the crab *Cancer pagurus* may have 'bile salts' containing substances such as decanoyl sarcosyl taurate (48).

$$CH_3(CH_2)_8CO \cdot N(CH_3) \cdot CH_2 \cdot CO \cdot NH(CH_2)_2SO_3^-$$

(48) Decanoyl sarcosyl taurate

Compounds of this type ought to function effectively as detergents, but whether they can (or are required to) have the other properties suggested in Chapter One as important in bile salts has not been determined. In any case, there is no evidence that any invertebrate can convert cholesterol to bile salts. Invertebrates also have no, or at most minimal, ability to biosynthesize cholesterol itself (Clayton, 1964).

7.3 Cyclostomata

The hagfishes are regarded as the most primitive living craniate chordates, both in the low level of organization they show and also in a biochemical sense (Brodal & Fänge, 1963): the chemical nature of myxinol (formula, p. 22) is certainly compatible with this view.

The molecule of myxinol is primitive in that it still has the full C_{27} skeleton and also the C-3β OH of cholesterol; thus it is, chemically, closer to cholesterol than any other bile alcohol except perhaps latimerol. Moreover, myxinol is the only apparently fully functional bile alcohol containing no more than four OH groups; it is also the only bile alcohol existing as a disulphate ester. It seems plausible to suggest that two sulphate groups are needed to convert such a tetrol into a sufficiently effective detergent. In models the 3β,7α,16α-hydroxyl groups of myxinol, in contrast to the 3α, 7α, 12α groups found in almost all other bile salts, are not particularly well differentiated from the less polar part of the molecule and are not so spaced as, apparently, to favour hydration.

In short, the principal hagfish bile salt does not, by comparison with those from more advanced vertebrates, look like a particularly effective detergent, and it may, as a speculation, be suggested that it is for this reason that it is present in the hagfish in such large amounts.

Myxinol has the C-5β (ring A/B *cis*) configuration, and since the Myxinidae are probably primarily (and perhaps solely) marine in origin, this configuration in bile salts may have arisen very early in the evolution of salt-water vertebrates.

The other family of cyclostomes, Petromyzonidae (lampreys), also have bile, at least in the larval (ammocoete) stages, but so far insufficient has been collected for chemical examination.

7.4 Chondrichthyes

There is some discussion about the origins of the chimaeras (e.g. Patterson, 1965), and the nature of their bile salts seems to support the view that these 'rabbit fishes' are closely related to the elasmobranchs (sharks and rays). Chimaerol (formula, p. 22) is 27- (or 26-) deoxy scymnol, and a single enzymic step would convert it into scymnol (formula, p. 19). Moreover, *Chimaera monstrosa* bile probably does contain scymnol, and at least one ray has chimaerol. Neither chimaerol nor scymnol has been found elsewhere in nature; their presence in Chondrichthyes emphasizes the isolation of these fishes from other vertebrate groups.

Both chondrichthean bile alcohols have the complete cholic acid nucleus and allo (C-5α) bile salts have not been found in these animals which, like the Myxinidae, are probably primarily marine.

Although cholic acid has been found in shark bile, it has not so far been shown to be of endogenous origin; the question whether bile salt evolution is likely to lead to cholic acid in elasmobranchs is therefore still open.

7.5 Osteichthyes

CROSSOPTERYGII. The most primitive of these is the so-called 'living fossil', the coelacanth *Latimeria chalumnae*. Except for myxinol, latimerol (structure, p. 22) is the bile alcohol chemically nearest to cholesterol and has the C-3β OH group of that substance. However, the 3,7,12 hydroxylation pattern is present. The configuration at C-5 is α, i.e. allo, and since the coelacanths, though now marine, had a long history in fresh water, it may be tentatively suggested that allo bile salts are an indication of a freshwater vertebrate ancestry. *Latimeria* bile also contains 5α-cyprinol (the 3α epimer of latimerol), so that the enzymes capable of inverting the C-3 hydroxyl group of cholesterol are already present in this primitive species.

The side-chain hydroxylation pattern in latimerol and 5α-cyprinol is quite different from that in the Chondrichthyes discussed above.

CHONDROSTEI. The sturgeons and closely related paddlefish have advanced to the extent that the principal bile salt is taurocholate; minor amounts of taurine-conjugated allocholic acid are also present. There is also a small proportion of a mixture of bile alcohols, probably as their sulphate esters. In one sturgeon, at least, the principal bile alcohol is 5β-cyprinol (structure, p. 22), and the rest of the alcohol mixture probably includes tetrols of both the 5α and 5β configuration. Such tetrols, at least as their monosulphates, could probably not act effectively as bile salts and it may be suggested that the relict amounts of bile alcohols in chondrostean bile, having indeed ceased to be functionally important, have failed to retain their chemical fitness for a role as bile salts: an anatomical analogy is the uselessness of limbs and other structures that during the course of evolution have failed to retain function and become vestigial.

In general, chondrostean bile salts are those to be expected of fishes largely advanced but still exhibiting primitive features and, if the arguments used above are sound, the presence of allo compounds is in accord with a freshwater history for these fishes.

HOLOSTEI. The bowfin *Amia calva* has taurocholate as almost its only bile salt, but allocholic acid was not found. These findings shed no light on the history or relationships of *Amia*, for bile salt evolution has here gone beyond its chemically informative stages.

TELEOSTEI. Bony fishes of the freshwater Order Ostariophysi include two main groups: cyprinids (including Cyprinidae, Catostomidae and Cobitidae) and silurids (including Siluridae and Bagridae). All the cyprinids investigated have 5α-cyprinol sulphate (formula, p. 22) as their chief bile salt; minor amounts of cholic acid (shown in the common carp *Cyprinus carpio* to be made from cholesterol) are also present. By contrast, the silurids have chiefly taurocholate, with perhaps in some species a certain amount of 5α-cyprinol. At first sight these facts suggest that cyprinids of the families investigated are evolutionarily primitive but are showing incipient advancement, whilst the silurids are altogether more advanced. This may indeed be true, but the argument leaves out the effect of diet. All the cyprinids examined are apparently vegetarian and omnivorous, whereas the silurids include forms that are more carnivorous. Thus, the selection pressure to advance from 5α-cyprinol may have been greater in the latter group.

Almost all the numerous other teleostean fishes listed have taurocholate as the chief bile salt; in some there are minor amounts of allocholic acid and among the Apodes (eels) there is a species having 5β-cyprinol and another containing C_{27} acids with the ring structure of cholic acid. A grey mullet has taurochenodeoxycholate as its chief bile salt, and this, by analogy with the mammals discussed later, may be ascribed to the vegetarian habits of these fish. On the whole, and except for the Ostariophysi, teleostean bile salts are not particularly informative, evolution to C_{24} acids having apparently taken place in all groups. Since it is inconceivable that any existing teleost could have given rise to amphibians or reptiles, the conclusion seems inescapable that these C_{24} acids must have arisen by evolution at least twice.

7.6 Amphibians

Very few amphibians have been investigated, but with remarkable results. The toad *Bufo vulgaris japonicus* ($= Bufo. b. formosus$) has the sulphate of 5β-bufol (formula, p. 23) as its chief bile salt, and this is probably true of the two other species of *Bufo* listed. The tetrahydroxy-cholestanes and acids are minor constituents, and a curious feature of the bile is that chromatography clearly shows that some of the acids are unconjugated, even in fresh bile from toads not visibly parasitized in the liver: their biosynthesis is discussed on p. 44. It is interesting that the side-chain hydroxylation pattern of bufol is also present in 5α-bufol from the newt, *Diemyctylus pyrrhogaster*. This genus of newts is common, and perhaps the bile salt found in one of them is an indication of their relationship to the Anura. Another salamander has allocholic acid and also 5α-cyprinol; these substances provide chemical links between this amphibian and the lizards and some of the fishes discussed above.

The Ranidae (frogs) are curious indeed. Two of them have the C_{26} ranol sulphates as chief bile salts, but *Rana nigromaculata* is entirely different, for it has 5β-cyprinol. The evolutionary or taxonomic significance of these facts seems impossible to assess at present. Some

of the frogs examined in detail can make both 3α,7α,12α-trihydroxyco-
prostanic and cholic acids, so that the bile salt picture in Ranidae is that
of an actively evolving and heterogenous group.

7.7 Reptiles

No bile alcohols have been found in vertebrates above the evolutionary
level of amphibia. The chemistry of reptilian bile acids is in agreement
with the suggestion that the Testudines originated from stock that has
been distinguishable from the remainder from the first appearance of
reptiles in the fossil record.

TESTUDINES. A characteristic bile salt in the turtles and tortoises is
the taurine conjugate of 3α,7α,12α,22ξ-tetrahydroxycoprostanic acid
(formula (21), p. 18, with ⁻OH for ⁻H at C-22). Chromatography suggests that this substance is present in several members of the group, and
it has not been detected elsewhere in nature. The other, unidentified,
bile acids in Testudines have likewise not been shown to occur in other
vertebrates.

SAURIA. Members of one group of these, the Diploglossa, differ
markedly from the rest examined. Monitor lizards (Varanidae) have
varanic acid, and a closely related substance (perhaps a stereoisomer) is
present in the poisonous lizard *Heloderma horridum*. Varanic acid is
probably 3α,7α,12α,24ξ-tetrahydroxycoprostanic acid, and so represents a stage in cholic acid biosynthesis beyond 3α,7α,12α-trihydroxyco-
prostanic acid (see p. 42). It has not been detected except in Varanidae.

The other lizards examined seem to have mainly taurine conjugates
of allocholic or cholic acids, and the anole *Anolis lineatopus* has tauroallo-
cholate as almost its only bile salt. Thus, these reptiles have all evolved
so as to possess C_{24} bile acids; the biosynthesis of these in lizards has
not been studied.

SERPENTES. In the snakes, also, only C_{24} bile acids have been found,
but two unusual substances are pythocholic (3α,12α,16α-trihydroxy-
cholanic) acid of the primitive family Boidae and perhaps also of
Aniliidae, and 3α,7α,12α,23ξ-tetrahydroxycholanic acid of certain Colu-
bridae and Viperidae. Pythocholic acid is a response to deoxycholic acid
formed by intestinal micro-organisms from the primary cholic acid

Chapter Five), and Dr Garth Underwood has suggested on taxonomic grounds that bitocholic ($3\alpha,12\alpha,23\xi$-trihydroxycholanic) acid may have a similar origin. If this is so, then the $3\alpha,7\alpha,12\alpha,23\xi$-tetrahydroxycholanic acid detected in the snakes listed is formed incidentally by C-23 hydroxylation of cholic acid; the chief bile salt being taurobitocholate. This suggestion has been partially tested, and bitocholic found to be the chief bile acid, only in the genus *Bitis*. Only small amounts of allocholic acid have so far been found in snakes. Some snakes may, like rats and mice, re-hydroxylate deoxycholic acid at C-7α to reform cholic acid; such a process could be detected experimentally.

The Crocodilia examined have $3\alpha,7\alpha,12\alpha$-trihydroxycoprostanic acid, and some also a $3\alpha,7\alpha$-dihydroxycoprostanic acid; C_{24} acids have not been found, and an alligator with a bile fistula did not make cholic acid from ^{14}C-4-cholesterol. Thus, the bile acids of archosaurs seemed to have evolved to a well-known C_{27} precursor (in mammals) of cholic acid, but not further than this.

7.8 Birds

In the few birds investigated in detail the chief bile acids are cholic and chenodeoxycholic, with allocholic acid in substantial amounts at least in penguins. The observation that chenodeoxycholic is the chief bile acid in vegetarian birds like the domestic fowl and goose, whilst there are much greater proportions of cholic/allocholic acid in the fish-eating penguins agrees with the views concerning adaptations to diet noticed in mammals and also to some extent in teleostean fish. There are a number of unidentified bile acids in birds, and the picture in these animals is fragmentary.

7.9 Mammals

MONOTREMES. Evolution of bile salts in these egg-laying forms seems to have proceeded to the common C_{24} acids; no C_{27} acids have been found, and glycine conjugates are absent. Thus, the bile salt chemistry is unhelpful to students of the evolution of this group.

MARSUPIALS. These animals have also little or no glycine conjugation; even the very strictly herbivorous koala bear has only taurine conjugates, albeit of a 'vegetarian' type of bile acid (3α-hydroxy-7-oxocholanic acid). Apart from this acid, which may or may not be a microbial artifact in the koala, marsupials have so far been found to have only the common cholic and chenodeoxycholic acids and the secondary deoxycholic acid.

EUTHERIANS. For the most part these animals have cholic and chenodeoxycholic acids as primary bile acids and both glycine and taurine conjugates occur. A detailed description of the biochemical situation in man is given in Chapter Six.

There is, except in Bovidae, an obvious relationship between bile salt types and diet in eutherian mammals. Carnivores have taurine conjugates and predominantly trihydroxy acids, herbivores have dihydroxy and sometimes also hydroxy-keto acids, often as glycine conjugates, and omnivores have a good proportion of all these kinds of bile salt. Why the bovids should depart from this pattern is not apparent; undoubtedly they do: for example, the ruminant ox, goat and sheep have bile salts very similar to those of omnivorous man himself.

The interesting case of the laboratory rabbit is mentioned in Chapter Five. This animal has little or no ability to biosynthesize chenodeoxycholic acid and relies on its intestinal microflora to maintain, by deoxygenation of cholic acid, the deoxycholic acid that, as its glycine conjugate, is almost the sole constituent of the bile salts. The pig similarly has a high proportion of hyodeoxycholic ($3\alpha,6\alpha$-dihydroxycholanic) acid made by micro-organisms from hyocholic acid and conjugated chiefly with glycine.

In addition to these broad differences, some groups of mammals have evolved unique bile acids, probably by additional hydroxylation of chenodeoxycholic acid. Thus, all the Pinnipedia apparently have phocaecholic ($3\alpha,7\alpha,23\xi$-trihydroxycholanic) acid, pigs (Suidae) have hyocholic ($3\alpha,6\alpha,7\alpha$-trihydroxycholanic) acid and rats and mice (Murinae) have α- and β- muricholic ($3\alpha,6\beta,7\alpha$- and $3\alpha,6\beta,7\beta$-trihydroxycholanic) acids. It may be that the ancestors of these various animals, beginning with cholic and chenodeoxycholic acids, reached a stage in which chenodeoxycholic was the main bile acid and then were impelled by some change in their circumstances to revert to a mainly trihydroxy bile acid type. It might then have been biochemically more expedient to exploit a liver enzymic system hydroxylating chenodeoxycholic acid at C-23, C-6α or C-6β rather than to re-develop the biosynthetic pathway leading to cholic acid. However, the Pinnipedia and Murinae now have cholic acid as a chief bile acid, so that re-development of its biosynthesis may have occurred later, perhaps in the case of the Murinae with partial suppression of the 6β-hydroxylation of chenodeoxycholic acid. These speculative ideas can perhaps be tested experimentally; the existence of 'unique' bile acids in mammals is certainly provocative.

7.10 Conclusions

It is obvious that bile salt differences can be used taxonomically, and for this they have advantages. A chemical character is precise, and in this case the molecules concerned are small and well understood. However, the situation is now open to study at a time when many differences have been obliterated by evolution, and in whole large groups nothing can be found except one or two common bile acids. Thus, taxonomically, this character is 'coarse' and perhaps useful only in broad fields and in certain special instances.

A more interesting reason for studying variations in bile salts is that they may perhaps throw light on the nature of evolution itself. Out-standing general questions, such as the reasons for evolutionary vigour (apparent in Ranidae) and senescence (e.g. in Crocodilia), may be approached biochemically and an answer may be sought to the question why in most vertebrate groups there seems to be a tendency to evolve to cholic acid.

A particularly intriguing finding is that in several genera (for example, *Latimeria, Cyprinus, Rana*) small amounts of what must be regarded as more 'modern' (advanced) bile salts may be found, although the bile salts as a whole are primitive. The processes by which these 'newer' substances, at first present in quantities too small to confer any selective advantage, come at last to dominate and finally eliminate the original bile salts are perhaps also important processes in evolution as a whole; there seems to be no reason why they should not be susceptible to bio-chemical study.

The bile salts are the end-products of quite complex enzymic pro-cesses: when the chemical nature of the enzymes themselves and then of the RNA and DNA concerned in their production have been elucidated there seems good reason to hope that the results will be of great value to students of evolution.

REFERENCES

Brodal, A. & Fänge, R. (1963) *The Biology of Myxine.* Oslo: Universitetsforlaget.
Clayton, R. B. (1964) *J. Lipid Res.*, **5**, 3.
Patterson, C. (1965) *Phil. Trans. R. Soc. B.*, **249**, 101.
Vonk, H. J. (1962) *Arch. int. Physiol.*, **70**, 67.

Bile salts in different animal forms

Most references are given in Haslewood (1962 or 1964); the remainder below.
e Indicates chromatographic evidence only: this is generally true of taurine and glycine in conjugates. Chromatographic evidence does not, unless otherwise indicated, distinguish between allocholic and cholic acids.

Higher class of animal	Species	Bile alcohols or acids isolated from bile	Type of conjugate	References*
INVERTEBRATES				
CRUSTACEA	Edible crab, *Cancer pagurus*	Decanoic, 5-dodecenoic and other fatty acids	Taurine, sarcosine	Van den Oord *et al.* (1965)
	Crayfish, *Procambarus clarkii*	Not steroids		Yamasaki *et al.* (1965)
VERTEBRATES				
FISHES				
AGNATHA				
Cyclostomata	Hagfish, *Myxine glutinosa* and *Eptatretus stoutii*	Myxinol	Sulphate (2 groups)	
CHONDRICHTHYES				
HOLOCEPHALI	*Chimaera monstrosa*	Chimaerol; (?) scymnol	Sulphate	
ELASMOBRANCHII				
Pleurotremata	Sharks, *Galeocerdo arcticus; Squalus acanthias; S. suckleyi Isurus glaucus*	Anhydroscymnol	Sulphate	
	Somniosus microcephalus	Anhydroscymnol; scymnol	Sulphate	

Hypotremata	? Two species of shark	Anhydroscymnol; cholic acid; ?a C_{27} acid	—	U.o.
	Centrophorus sp.	Scymnol Anhydroscymnol	Sulphate	
	Skate, Raia batis	Anhydroscymnol	Sulphate	
	Ray, Dasyuatis akajei	Anhydrochimaerol; anhydroscymnol; cholic acid	—	
OSTEICHTHYES				
CHOANICHTHYES				
Crossopterygii	Coelacanth, Latimeria chalumnae	Latimerol; 5α-cyprinol	Sulphate	
Dipnoi	Lungfish, Protopterus aethiopicus	5α-Cyprinol	Sulphate	U.o.
ACTINOPTERYGII				
CHONDROSTEI				
Acipenseridae	Sturgeon, Acipenser huso	Allocholic acid; cholic acid; 5β-cyprinol; other alcohols	Taurine; sulphate	U.o.
	Acipenser stellatus; A. guldenstädti	Allocholic acid; cholic acid; alcohols	Taurine; sulphate	U.o.
Polyodontidae	Paddlefish, Polyodon spathula	Allocholic acid; cholic acid; alcohols	Taurine; sulphate	U.o.
HOLOSTEI				
TELEOSTEI	Bowfin, Amia calva	Cholic acid	Taurine	U.o.
Ostariophysi				
Cyprinidae	Carp, Cyprinus carpio	5α-Cyprinol; 27-deoxy-5α-cyprinol; cholic acid	Sulphate; taurine	Ref. [11], Table 2.5
	Tench, Tinca tinca; Chub, Leuciscus cephalus; Roach, Rutilus rutilus	5α-Cyprinol	Sulphate	

* Where not given in Haslewood (1962 or 1964) U.o. refers to unpublished observations in the author's laboratory.

APPENDIX—*continued*

Higher class of animal	Species	Bile alcohols or acids isolated from bile	Type of conjugate	References *
Ostariophysi Cyprinidae	'Hasu', *Opsariichthys uncirostris*; 'Kamatsuka', *Pseudogobio esocinus*; 'Wataka', *Ishikauia steenackeri*; 'Nigoi', *Hemibarbus barbus*; 'Oikawa', *Zacco platypus*; 'Higai', *Sarcocheilichthys variegatus*; 'Ugi', *Tribolodon h. hakonensis*; Goldfish, 'Funa', *Carassius carassius*	5α-Cyprinol; cholic acid (minor amounts)	Sulphate; taurine	Ref. [13], Table 2.5
Catostomidae	Sucker, *Catostomus commersoni*	5α-Cyprinol	Sulphate	*U.o.*
Cobitidae	*Misgurnus anguillicaudatus*	? Cyprinol	Sulphate	
Siluridae	Catfish, *Silurus glanis* *Parasilurus asotus*	Cholic acid Cholic acid; chenodeoxy-cholic acid	Taurine Taurine	*U.o.*
Bagridae	'Gigi' fish, *Pelteobagrus nudiceps*	Allocholic acid; cholic acid	Taurine	
Serrasalmidae	Piranha, *Serrasalmus ternetzi*	Cholic acid	—	*U.o.*
OTHER TELEOSTEI Isospondyli	Herring, *Clupea harengus* Anchovy, *Engraulis japonicus*	Cholic acid Cholic acid; chenodeoxy-cholic acid	Taurine Taurine	*U.o.*

		Cholic acid	Taurine	
	Salmo kisutch (=*Oncorhynchus*); *Plecoglossus altivelis*		Taurine	*U.o.*
HAPLOMI **Apodes**	Pike, *Esox lucius*	Cholic acid	Taurine	
	Eel, *Anguilla japonica*	Cholic acid; chenodeoxycholic acid; two C_{27} lactone-forming acids having the cholic acid nucleus	Taurine	
	Conger myriaster (=*Astroconger*)	5β-Cyprinol; cholic acid; 3α,7β,12α-trihydroxy-cholanic acid; chenodeoxycholic acid	Taurine	**Ref. [12], Table 2.5;** Yukawa (1965)
	Anago anago; Muraenesox cinereus	Cholic acid	Taurine	
SYNENTOGNATHI	Garfish, *Belone belone*	Cholic acid	Taurine	
Acanthopterygii ANACANTHINII	Cod, *Gadus callarias*	Cholic acid; ? deoxycholic acid	Taurine	
	Pacific cod, *Gadus macrocephalus*	Cholic acid	Taurine	
	Theragra chalcogramma	Cholic acid; chenodeoxycholic acid	Taurine	
Percomorphi	*Stereolepis ischinagi*	Cholic acid	Taurine	
	Pagrosomus major	Cholic acid	Taurine	
	Sparus macrocephalus (=*Milio*); *Siganus fuscescens; Sciaena mitsukuri* (=*Nibea*)	Cholic acid; chenodeoxycholic acid	Taurine	

* Where not given in Haslewood (1962 or 1964). *U.o.* refers to unpublished observations in the author's laboratory.

APPENDIX—continued

Higher class of animal	Species	Bile alcohols or acids isolated from bile	Type of conjugate	References *
Percomorphi	Tunny, *Thunnus thynnus*; *Scomberomorus niphonius*	Cholic acid	Taurine	
	Enthynnus pelamis (=*Katsuwonus*)	Cholic acid; chenodeoxy-cholic acid	Taurine	
	Mackerel, *Scomber scombrus*	Cholic acid; chenodeoxy-cholic acid^c	Taurine	*U.o.*
	Swordfish, *Xiphias gladius*	Cholic acid	Taurine	
	Seriola quinqueradiata	Cholic acid; ? steroid $C_{24}H_{42}O_5$	Taurine	
	Periopthalamus cantonensis; *Acanthogobius flavimanus*	Cholic acid; chenodeoxy-cholic acid	Taurine	
	Grey mullet, *Mugil cephalus*	Cholic acid; chenodeoxy-cholic acid	Taurine	
	Mugil sp.	Chenodeoxycholic acid; cholic acid^c	Taurine	*U.o.*
SCLEROPAREI	*Sebastodes matsubarae*; *S. inermis*	Cholic acid; chenodeoxy-cholic acid	Taurine	
	Inimicus japonicus	Allocholic acid; cholic acid; chenodeoxycholic acid	Taurine	
HETEROSOMATA	Turbot, *Scophthalamus rhombus*	Cholic acid	Taurine	
	Paralichthys olivaceus	Cholic acid; chenodeoxy-cholic acid	Taurine	
	Plaice, *Pleuronectes platessa*	Cholic acid	Taurine	
PLECTOGNATHII	*Monocanthus cirrifer* (=*Stephanolepsis*)	Cholic acid; chenodeoxy-cholic acid	Taurine	
	Tetrodon porphyleus	Allocholic acid; cholic acid	Taurine	

Taxonomy untraced			
'Bari'	Allocholic acid; cholic acid; chenodeoxycholic acid	—	
'Beisuke'	Cholic acid; chenodeoxycholic acid	Taurine	
AMPHIBIANS			
Caudata			
Newt, *Diemyctylus pyrrhogaster*	5α-Bufol; cholic acid; deoxycholic acid	Sulphate	Ref. [13], Table 2.5 Amimoto (1966)
Salamander, *Megalobatrachus japonicus*	5α-Cyprinol; a trihydroxy C_{27} acid; allocholic acid	Sulphate; taurine	*U.o.*
Fire salamander, *Salamandra salamandra*	Alcohols; allocholic acid	Sulphate; taurine	
Anura			
Toad, *Bufo vulgaris japonicus* (= *Bufo b. formosus*)	5β-Bufol; 3α,7α,12α,27-tetrahydroxy-5α- and -5β-cholestane; trihydroxybufosterocholenic acid; 3α,7α,12α-trihydroxycoprostanic and -coprost-23-enic acid	Sulphate	Ref. [14], Table 2.5
Bufo b. bufo; B. marinus; B. regularis	5β-Bufol[c]	Sulphate	*U.o.*
Frog, *Rana temporaria*	5α-Ranol	Sulphate	
Rana catesbiana	5α- and 5β-Ranol; 3α,7α,12α-trihydroxycoprostanic acid; dihydroxycoprostanic acid; cholic acid	Sulphate; taurine	
Rana nigromaculata	5β-Cyprinol; 3α,7α,12α-trihydroxycoprostanic acid; cholic acid	Sulphate; taurine	Ref. [16], Table 2.5
Rana ridibunda	3α,7α,12α-Trihydroxy-coprostanic acid[c]	Taurine	*U.o.*

* Where not given in Haslewood (1962 or 1964). *U.o.* refers to unpublished observations in the author's laboratory.

Higher class of animal	Species	Bile alcohols or acids isolated from bile	Type of conjugate	References *
REPTILES				
Testudines				
CRYPTODIRA				
Testudinoidea				
Chelydridae	Snapping turtle, *Macroclemmys temminckii*	(Prob.) $3\alpha,7\alpha,12\alpha,22\xi$-tetrahydroxycoprostanic acid[c]; other acids[c]	Taurine	*U.o.*
Emydidae	*Clemmys insculpta*; *Pseudemys ornata*	As above	Taurine	*U.o.*
	European pond tortoise, *Emys orbicularis*	Tetrahydroxysterocholanic ($3\alpha,7\alpha,12\alpha,22\xi$-tetrahydroxycoprostanic) acid; tetrahydroxyisosterocholanic acid[c]	Taurine	Amimoto *et al.* (1965)
Testudinidae	*Testudo elephantopus* (= *vicina*)	Unidentified acids[c]	Taurine	*U.o.*
	Greek tortoise, *Testudo graeca*	(Prob.) $3\alpha,7\alpha,12\alpha,22\xi$-tetrahydroxycoprostanic acid[c]; other acids[c]	Taurine	*U.o.*
Chelonioidea				
Cheloniidae	Green turtle, *Chelone mydas*	(Prob.) $3\alpha,7\alpha,12\alpha,22\xi$-tetrahydroxycoprostanic acid; other acids[c]	Taurine	*U.o.*

88

			Taurine	Animoto et al. (1965)
Trionychoidea Trionychidae	Soft shelled turtle, *Trionyx sinensis* (=*japonica*, *Amyda*)	Tetrahydroxysterocholanic $(3\alpha,7\alpha,12\alpha,22\xi$-tetra-hydroxycoprostanic) acid; tetrahydroxy-isosterocholanic acid; heterocholanic acid		
	Trionyx cartilagineus (=*phayeri*); *T. triunguis*	(Prob.) $3\alpha,7\alpha,12\alpha,22\xi$-tetra-hydroxycoprostanic acid[c]; other acids[c]	Taurine	U.o.
PLEURODIRA Pelomedusidae	*Pelusios sinuatus*	Unidentified acids[c]	Taurine	U.o.
Sauria GEKKOTA Pygopodidae	*Lialis burtonis*	Cholic acid[c]	Taurine	U.o.
IGUANIA Iguanidae	*Anolis lineatopus*	Allocholic acid; cholic acid (trace)	Taurine	U.o.
	Anolis garmani; A. grahami; A. richardi; Cyclura carinata; Polychrus marmoratus	Allocholic/cholic acid[c]; other acids[c]	Taurine	U.o.
Agamidae	*Amphibolurus barbatus; Physignathus lesueri; Uromastix thomasi*	As above[c]	Taurine	U.o.
Chameleontidae	*Chameleo muelleri*	As above[c]	Taurine	U.o.
LEPTOGLOSSA Teiidae	*Ameiva ameiva*	As above[c]	Taurine	U.o.

89

* Where not given in Haslewood (1962 or 1964). *U.o.* refers to unpublished observations in the author's laboratory.

APPENDIX—*continued*

Higher class of animal	Species	Bile alcohols or acids isolated from bile	Type of conjugate	References*
Sauria				
DIPLOGLOSSA				
Varanidae	Monitors, *Varanus niloticus*; *V. gouldi*	Varanic acid; other acids	Taurine	*U.o. (V. gouldi)*
	Varanus griseus; *V. salvator*; *V. varius*	Varanic acid[c]; other acids[c]	Taurine	*U.o.*
Helodermatidae	Beaded lizard, *Heloderma horridum*	Acid very like varanic acid	Taurine	*U.o.*
AMPHISBAENIA				
Trogonophidae	*Agamodon anguliceps*	Allocholic/cholic acid[c]; other acids[c]	Taurine	*U.o.*
Serpentes				
SCOLECOPHIDIA				
Typhlopidae	*Typhlops jamaicensis*	Cholic acid	Taurine	*U.o.*
HENOPHIDIA				
Aniliidae	*Cylindrophis rufus*	(Prob.) Pythocholic acid	Taurine	*U.o.*
Boidae	*Python reticulatus*	Cholic acid; pythocholic acid; 3α,12α-dihydroxy-7-oxocholanic acid	Taurine	
	Python molurus; *P. sebae*	Pythocholic acid	Taurine	
	Boa constrictor constrictor; *B. c. imperator*; *Epicrates cenchria*	Pythocholic acid	Taurine	
	Boa constrictor occidentalis; *Corallus canina*; *Eunectes murinus*	Cholic acid; pythocholic acid	Taurine	
	Corallus enhydris	Cholic acid[c]	Taurine	*U.o.*

90

	Pythocholic acid	Cholic acid	Taurine	U.o.
Eryx conicus (=*Gongylophis*); *E. jaculus*; *E. johnii*	Pythocholic acid[c]		Taurine	U.o.
Acrochordidae: *Acrochordus javanicus*; *Chersydrus granulatus*		Cholic acid[c]	Taurine	U.o.
CAENOPHIDIA Colubridae: *Elaphe quadrivirgata*; *E. carinata*; *Boiga dendrophila*; *Drymarchon corais couperi*		Cholic acid	Taurine	
Anaetulla nasuta (=*Dryophis*); *Boiga blandingi*; *Coluber constrictor mormon*; *C. ravergieri*; *C. viridiflavus*; *Crotaphopeltis natamboeia*; *Dipsas variegata trinitas*; *Dispholidus typus*; *Duberria lutrix*; *Elaphe moellendorfi*; *E. quatorlineata*; *E. situla*; *E. taeniurus*; *Lampropeltis getulus*; *Malpolon monspesselana*; *Natrix natrix*; *Philodryas olfersi* (=*Chlorosoma*); *Philothamnus hoplogaster* (=*Chlorophis*); *Pituophis sayi*; *Psammophis condanarus*; *P. sibilans*; *Ptyas mucosus*; *Rhamphiophis*		Cholic acid[c]	Taurine	U.o.

* Where not given in Haslewood (1962 or 1964). *U.o.* refers to unpublished observations in the author's laboratory.

Higher class of animal	Species	Bile alcohols or acids isolated from bile	Type of conjugate	References *
Serpentes				
Colubridae	nostratus; Telescopus fallax (=Tarbophis); Thelotornis kirtlandi; Xenochrophis piscator (=Fowlea)			
	Enhydris enhydris (=Hypsirhina); E. pakistanica; E. plumbea; Helicops angulatus; Homalopsis buccata; Pseudoboa cloelia; P. newwiedi; P. pelota	$3\alpha,7\alpha,12\alpha,23\xi$-tetra-hydroxycholanic acid[c]	Taurine	U.o.
Elapidae	Bungarus multitinctus; Dendroapsis viridis; Naja nivea	Cholic acid	Taurine	
	Bungarus fasciatus; Dendroapsis augusticeps; D. jamesoni kaimosae; Enhydrina schistosa; Hemachatus haemachatus (=Serpedon); Hydrophis cyanocinctus; Naja goldi; N. haje; N. melanoleuca; N. naja; N. ngricollis; Notechis scutatus; Pseudechis porphyriacus	Cholic acid[c]	Taurine	U.o.

Viperidae Viperinae	*Cerastes cerastes; Echis carinatus*	Cholic acid[c]	Taurine	*U.o.*
	Bitis lachesis (=arietans); B. gabonica; Vipera russelli	$3\alpha,7\alpha,12\alpha,23\xi$-Tetra-hydroxycholanic acid; allocholic acid; (prob.) cholic acid; bitocholic acid	Taurine	*U.o.* (*V. russelli*)
	Atheris squamiger; Bitis nasicornis; B. worthing-toni; Eristocophis mac-mahoni; Vipera ammody-tes; V. berus; V. palae-stinae	$3\alpha,7\alpha,12\alpha,23\xi$-Tetra-hydroxycholanic acid[c]; other acids[c]	Taurine	*U.o.*
Crotalinae	*Crotalus terrificus; C. hor-ridus; C. oregonus*	Cholic acid	Taurine	
	Agkistrodon piscivorus; Bothrops alternatus; Crotalus adamanteus; C. atrox; C. confluentes; Lachesis muta; Trimere-surus wagleri; T. rhom-beatus	Cholic acid[c]	Taurine	*U.o.*
Crocodilia Crocodylidae	*Alligator mississipiensis*	$3\alpha,7\alpha,12\alpha$-Trihydroxy-coprostanic acid; $3\alpha,7\alpha$-dihydroxycoprostanic acid	Taurine	Dean & Whitehouse (1966): $3\alpha,7\alpha$-di-hydroxy-coprostanic acid

93

* Where not given in Haslewood (1962 or 1964). *U.o.* refers to unpublished observations in the author's laboratory.

Higher class of animal	Species	Bile alcohols or acids isolated from bile	Type of conjugate	References*
Crocodilia	*Caiman crocodilus; Crocodylus acutus; C. johnsonii; C. niloticus*	$3\alpha,7\alpha,12\alpha$-Trihydroxy-coprostanic acid; other acids	Taurine	*U.o.* (*C. acutus*)
BIRDS *RATITES* **Rheiformes**	*Rhea americana*	Cholic acid[c]; chenodeoxycholic acid[c]; other acids[c]	Taurine	*U.o.*
Casuariiformes	Emu, *Dromiceius n-hollandiae*	As above	Taurine	*U.o.*
CARINATES **Procellariiformes**	Petrel, *Ossifraga gigantea*	Allocholic acid[c]; cholic acid[c]; chenodeoxycholic acid[c]	Taurine	*U.o.*
Sphenisciformes	Penguins, *Aptenodites patagonica; Pygoscelis papua; P. antarctica; Spheniscus demersus; S. humboldti*	Allocholic acid; cholic acid; chenodeoxycholic acid; other acids	Taurine	*U.o.* and [c] (except *A. patagonica*)
Pelecaniformes	Gannet, *Sula bassana*	Cholic acid[c]; chenodeoxy-cholic acid[c]	Taurine	*U.o.*
Ciconiiformes	Shoebill stork, *Balaeniceps rex*	Chenodeoxycholic acid[c]; other acids[c]	Taurine	*U.o.*
	Flamingoes, *Phoenicopterus antiquorum; P. chilensis*	Allocholic acid[c]; cholic acid[c]; chenodeoxycholic acid[c]; other acids[c]	Taurine	*U.o.*
	Phoenicopterus minor;	Cholic acid[c]; chenodeoxy-cholic acid[c]	Taurine	*U.o.*

94

Order	Species	Bile acids		
Anseriformes	Domestic duck; *wigeon, Anas penelope*; Domestic goose	Cholic acid; chenodeoxycholic acid Chenodeoxycholic acid	—	
	Goose, *Anser rossi*;	Cholic acid[e]; chenodeoxycholic acid[e]; other acids[e]	Taurine	U.o.
	Swan, *Cygnus melancoriphus*	Chenodeoxycholic acid[e]; other acids[e]		U.o.
	Screamer, *Palamedea cornuta* (= *Anhima*)	As above	Taurine	U.o.
Falconiformes	Vulture, *Catharista urubu*	Cholic acid[e]; chenodeoxycholic acid[e]	Taurine	U.o.
	Vulture, *Gypaetus barbatus*	Cholic acid; chenodeoxycholic acid[e]; other acids[e]	Taurine	U.o.
	Eagles, *Cuncuma vocifer*; *Terathiopus ecaudatus*	Allocholic acid[e]; cholic acid[e]; chenodeoxycholic acid[e]; other acids[e]	Taurine	U.o.
	Kite, *Milvus l. lineatus*	Allocholic acid; cholic acid; chenodeoxycholic acid	—	
Galliformes	Curassow, *Mitu mitu*	Chenodeoxycholic acid[e]; other acids	Taurine	U.o.
	Peafowl, *Pavo cristatus*	Chenodeoxycholic acid	Taurine	U.o.
	Pavo muticus	Allocholic acid[e]; cholic acid[e]; chenodeoxycholic acid[e]	Taurine	U.o.
	Pheasant, *Phasianus colchicus karpowi*	Chenodeoxycholic acid	—	
	Turkey, *Meleagris gallopavo*	Cholic acid; chenodeoxycholic acid	—	

* Where not given in Haslewood (1962 or 1964). *U.o.* refers to unpublished observations in the author's laboratory.

Higher class of animal	Species	Bile alcohols or acids isolated from bile	Type of conjugate	References *
Galliformes	Domestic fowl	Allocholic acid; cholic acid; chenodeoxycholic acid; 'isolithocholic acid'; 3α-hydroxy-7-oxocholanic acid; 3-oxochola-4,6-dienic acid	Taurine	
Gruiformes	Crane, *Balearica pavonina*	Cholic acid[c]; chenodeoxycholic acid[c]	Taurine	*U.o.*
Strigiformes	Eagle owl, *Bubo bubo*	Cholic acid[c]; chenodeoxycholic acid[c]; other acids[c]	Taurine	*U.o.*
	Owl species	Cholic acid; chenodeoxycholic acid	—	
Coraciiformes	Hornbill, *Bycanistes cylindricus*	Unidentified acids[c]	Taurine	*U.o.*
Passeriformes	Crow, *Corvus coronoides japanensis*; Magpie, *Pica p. serica*	Cholic acid; chenodeoxycholic acid	Taurine	
MAMMALS PROTOTHERIA **Monotremata**	Platypus, *Ornithorhyncus anatinus*; Echidna, *Tachyglossus aculeatus*	Cholic acid; chenodeoxycholic acid; (prob.) deoxycholic acid	Taurine	
METATHERIA **Marsupalia** **Didelphidae**	Opossum, *Didelphis marsupialis virginiana*	Cholic acid; chenodeoxycholic acid	Taurine	

96

Phalangeridae	Koala, *Phascolarctos cinereus*	Chenodeoxycholic acid (trace); 3α-hydroxy-7-oxocholanic acid	Taurine	
Macropodidae	Kangaroo, *Macropus giganteus*	Cholic acid; chenodeoxycholic acid; deoxycholic acid	Taurine, (?) glycine	
	Macropus ruficollis	Cholic acid	Taurine	
	Macropus rufogriseus	Cholic acid[e]; deoxycholic acid	Taurine	*U.o.*
EUTHERIA				
Insectivora				
Erinaceidae	Hedgehog, *Erinaceus europaeus*	Cholic acid		
Primates				
Cebidae	Capuchin, *Cebus fatuellis*	Cholic acid; deoxycholic acid	Taurine	
	Cebus sp.	Cholic acid; chenodeoxycholic acid; deoxycholic acid	Taurine; glycine	
	Saimiri sp.	Cholic acid; chenodeoxycholic acid; deoxycholic acid; lithocholic acid	Taurine; glycine	
	Lagothrix sp.	As above	As above	
	'*Pithecus cyclopis*'	Cholic acid; chenodeoxycholic acid; deoxycholic acid[e]	Glycine	
Cercopithecidae	*Cercopithecus aethiops tantulus*; *C. nictitans martini*	Cholic acid; chenodeoxycholic acid; deoxycholic acid; 3α,12α-dihydroxy-7-oxocholanic acid	Taurine; glycine	

* Where not given in Haslewood (1962 or 1964). *U.o.* refers to unpublished observations in the author's laboratory.

Higher class of animal	Species	Bile alcohols or acids isolated from bile	Type of conjugate	References *
Primates				
Cercopithecidae	*Cercopithecus mona*	Cholic acid; chenodeoxycholic acid; deoxycholic acid; lithocholic acid	Taurine; glycine	
	Rhesus, *Macaca mulatta*	Cholic acid; chenodeoxycholic acid; deoxycholic acid; lithocholic acid	Taurine; glycine	
	Macaca irus	Allocholic acid; cholic acid; chenodeoxycholic acid[c]; deoxycholic acid[c]	Taurine	U.o.; Tammar (1966): allocholic acid; cholic acid
	Macaca maurus	Cholic acid; chenodeoxycholic acid; deoxycholic acid[c]	Taurine; glycine	U.o.
	Baboon, *Papio anubis* *Mandrillus leucophaeus*	Cholic acid Cholic acid	— —	
	Langur, *Simia satyrus*	Cholic acid; chenodeoxycholic acid; deoxycholic acid[c]	Taurine; glycine	U.o.
Pongidae	Chimpanzee, *Pan satyrus*	Cholic acid; chenodeoxycholic acid; deoxycholic acid	Taurine; glycine	
Hominidae	Man	Allocholic acid; cholic acid; chenodeoxycholic acid; deoxycholic acid; ursodeoxycholic acid; litho-	Taurine; glycine	Tammar (1966): allocholic acid Keto acids, p. 69

Edentata	Anteater, *Myrmecophaga tridactyla*	cholic acid; 3α,7α,12α-trihydroxycoprostanic acid Allocholic acid°; cholic acid°; chenodeoxycholic acid°; deoxycholic acid°	Taurine	*U.o.*; Tammar (1966): allo-cholic acid; cholic acid
Pholidota	Pangolins, *Manis penta-dactyla* and *M. tricuspis*	Cholic acid°; chenodeoxy-cholic acid°; deoxycholic acid°	Taurine	*U.o.*
Lagomorpha	Domestic rabbit, *Orycto-lagus cuniculus*	Cholic acid; allodeoxycholic acid; deoxycholic acid; lithocholic acid	Glycine	Table 2.1 (allo-deoxycholic acid)
	Hare, *Lepus timidus*	Deoxycholic acid	—	
	Lepus californicus	Cholic acid; chenodeoxy-cholic acid°; deoxycholic acid°	Taurine; glycine	*U.o.*
Rodentia Sciuridae	Ground squirrel, *Citellus mongolicus ramosus*	Cholic acid	Taurine	
Castoridae	Beaver, *Castor canadensis*	? Cholic acid; chenodeoxy-cholic acid°; deoxycholic acid°	Taurine (trace); glycine	*U.o.*
Cricetidae	Golden hamster, *Cricetus auratus*	Cholic acid; chenodeoxy-cholic acid; deoxycholic acid	Taurine; glycine	
Muridae	Laboratory rat	Cholic acid; chenodeoxy-cholic acid; ursodeoxy-cholic acid; α- and β-muricholic acids	Taurine; glycine	

99

* Where not given in Haslewood (1962 or 1964). *U.o.* refers to unpublished observations in the author's laboratory.

APPENDIX—*continued*

Higher class of animal	Species	Bile alcohols or acids isolated from bile	Type of conjugate	References [*]
Rodentia				
Muridae	Laboratory mouse	Cholic acid; α- and β-muricholic acids		
Caviidae	Guinea-pig	Cholic acid; chenodeoxycholic acid; (prob.) ursodeoxycholic acid; 3α-hydroxy-7-oxo-, 7α-hydroxy-3-oxo- and 3-7-dioxocholanic acids; lithocholic acid; 2 neutral steroids	Taurine; glycine	Danielsson & Einarsson 1964); Schoenfield & Sjövall (1966)
Capromyidae	Coypu, *Myocastor coypus*	Cholic acid; chenodeoxycholic acid; ursodeoxycholic acid; 3α-hydroxy-7-oxocholanic acid	Taurine; glycine	
Echimyidae	*Proechimys* sp.	Cholic acid[e]; chenodeoxycholic acid[e]	Glycine	*U.o.*
Thyronomidae	Cutting-grass, *Thryonomys swinderianus*	Chenodeoxycholic acid; deoxycholic acid; (prob.) ursodeoxycholic acid	Taurine	
Cetacea	Fin whale, *Balaenoptera physalus*	Cholic acid; deoxycholic acid	Taurine; glycine	
	Balaenoptera sibbaldi; *B. borealis*	Cholic acid	Taurine	
Carnivora				
FISSIPEDA				
Canidae	Dog, (incl. *Canis familiaris*)	Cholic acid; chenodeoxycholic acid; deoxycholic acid	Taurine	

	Cholic acid	Taurine	
Dhole, *Canis dukhunensis* Wolf, *Canis lupus*	Cholic acid; chenodeoxy-cholic acid	Glycine	
Fox, *Vulpes pecculiosus*	Cholic acid; deoxycholic acid	—	
Nyctereutes viverrinus (=*procyonides*) Guara, *Chrysocyon brachyurus*	Cholic acid[e]; chenodeoxy-cholic acid[e]; deoxycholic acid[e]	Taurine; glycine (trace)	*U.o.*
Himalayan bear, *Selenarctos tibetanus*	Cholic acid[e]; chenodeoxy-cholic acid[e]; deoxycholic acid[e]	Taurine	*U.o.*
Ursidae *Ursus arctos isabellinus*	? Deoxycholic acid	Glycine	
Ursus thibetanus japonicus	Chenodeoxycholic acid; ursodeoxycholic acid	—	
Japanese bear	Cholic acid; chenodeoxy-cholic acid; ursodeoxy-cholic acid	Taurine; glycine	
Ursus americanus	Cholic acid; chenodeoxy-cholic acid[e]; deoxycholic acid[e]	Taurine	*U.o.*
Polar bear, *Thalarctos maritimus*	Cholic acid; chenodeoxy-cholic acid; deoxycholic acid[e]; ursodeoxycholic acid	Taurine	*U.o.* (deoxy-cholic acid)
Helarctos malayamus	Cholic acid; chenodeoxy-cholic acid[e]; deoxycholic acid[e]	Taurine	*U.o.* (except cholic acid)
Sloth bear, *Melursus ursinus*	Cholic acid; chenodeoxy-cholic acid; deoxycholic acid	Glycine	*U.o.*

* Where not given in Haslewood (1962 or 1964). *U.o.* refers to unpublished observations in the author's laboratory.

Higher class of animal	Species	Bile alcohols or acids isolated from bile	Type of conjugate	References*
Carnivora				
Procyonidae	Racoon, *Procyon lotor*	Cholic acid; chenodeoxycholic acid[c]; deoxycholic acid	Taurine; glycine	*U.o.* (chenodeoxycholic acid)
	Coati, *Nasua nasua*	Cholic acid; chenodeoxycholic acid[c]	Taurine	*U.o.* (except cholic acid)
Mustelidae	Weasel, *Mustela itati*	Cholic acid	—	
	Marten, *Martes m. melampus*	Cholic acid; deoxycholic acid	Taurine	
	Otter, *Lutra*	Cholic acid; deoxycholic acid	Taurine	
	Otter, *Amblonyx cinerea*	Cholic acid[c]; deoxycholic acid[c]	Taurine	*U.o.*
	Sea otter, *Enhydra lutris*	Cholic acid[c]	Taurine	*U.o.*
Viverridae	Mongoose, *Herpestes edwardsi*	Allocholic acid; cholic acid; chenodeoxycholic acid[c]; deoxycholic acid[c]	Taurine	*U.o.*; Tammar (1966): allocholic acid; cholic acid
	Kusimanse, *Crossarchus obscurus*	Cholic acid	—	
Felidae	Puma, *Felis concolor*	Allocholic acid; cholic acid; chenodeoxycholic acid[c]; deoxycholic acid[c]	Taurine	*U.o.*; Tammar (1966): allocholic acid; cholic acid
	Lion, *Felis leo*	Cholic acid; chenodeoxycholic acid[c]; deoxycholic acid[c]	Taurine	*U.o.* (except cholic acid and taurine)

	Bile acids	Conjugation	Notes*
Leopard, *Felis pardus*	Cholic acid; chenodeoxycholic acid[e]; deoxycholic acid[e]	Taurine	*U.o.* (except cholic acid and taurine)
Tiger, *Felis tigris*	Cholic acid; chenodeoxycholic acid[e]; deoxycholic acid[e]	Taurine	*U.o.*
Domestic cat	Cholic acid	Taurine	
Cheetah, *Acinonyx jubatus*	Cholic acid; chenodeoxycholic acid; deoxycholic acid[e]	Taurine	*U.o.* (except cholic acid)
PINNIPEDIA			
Otariidae			
Californian sea-lion, *Zalophus californianus*	Allocholic acid[e]; cholic acid[e]; phocaecholic acid; chenodeoxycholic acid[e]; deoxycholic acid[e]	Taurine	*U.o.* (except phocaecholic acid); Tammar (1966): allocholic acid; cholic acid
Stellar sea-lion, *Eumetopias jubata*	Cholic acid; acid (?) $C_{27}H_{46}O_6$	Taurine	
'Otaria ursina'	Cholic acid; phocaecholic acid	Taurine	
Odobenidae			
Walrus, *Odobenus rosmarus*	Cholic acid; phocaecholic acid	Taurine	
Phocidae			
Seals, *Phoca barbata; P. groenlandica; P. foetida; Cystophora cristata*	Cholic acid; phocaecholic acid	Taurine; glycine	
Phoca hispida	Phocaecholic acid	—	
Grey seal of the Baltic (? *Halichoerus grypus*)	$3\alpha,7\alpha,12\alpha,23\xi$-tetrahydroxycholanic acid; cholic acid; phocaecholic acid; chenodeoxycholic acid	—	

* Where not given in Haslewood (1962 or 1964). *U.o.* refers to unpublished observations in the author's laboratory.

Higher class of animal	Species	Bile alcohols or acids isolated from bile	Type of conjugate	References *
Carnivora	Leopard seal, *Hydrurga leptonyx*	$3\alpha,7\alpha,12\alpha,23\xi$-tetra-hydroxycholanic acid; allocholic acid; cholic acid; phocaecholic acid	—	
Tubulidentata	Aardvark, *Orycteropus afer*	Allocholic acid; cholic acid; chenodeoxycholic acid[e]; deoxycholic acid	Taurine	*U.o.*; Tammar (1966): allo-cholic acid; cholic acid
Proboscidea	Elephant	Cholic acid; deoxycholic acid	—	
Perissodactyla	Domestic horse	Cholic acid	—	
Artiodactyla Suidae 104	Domestic pig	? Cholic acid; hyocholic acid; chenodeoxycholic acid; hyodeoxycholic acid; $3\alpha,6\beta$- and $3\beta,6\alpha$-dihydroxycholanic acids, 3α-hydroxy-6-oxo-cholanic (or allocholanic) acid; lithocholic acid; ? C_{27} acids.	Taurine; glycine	
	Wild pig, *Sus leucomastyx* Abyssinian wild pig	Hyodeoxycholic acid Hyocholic acid; cheno-deoxycholic acid; hyodeoxycholic acid	Glycine Taurine; glycine	
	Wart-hog, *Phacochoerus aethiopicus*	Cholic acid; deoxycholic acid[e]; hyodeoxycholic acid	Taurine; glycine	*U.o.* (deoxy-cholic acid)

Hippopotamidae	Hippopotamus amphibius	Cholic acid; chenodeoxycholic acid; deoxycholic acid[c]	Taurine; glycine	U.o. (deoxycholic acid; conjugates)
Bovidae	Kudu, Strepsiceros imberbis	Cholic acid; chenodeoxycholic acid[c]; deoxycholic acid[c]	Taurine	U.o.
	Eland, Taurotragus oryx	Cholic acid	—	
	Water buffalo; Bubalus bubalus	Cholic acid; chenodeoxycholic acid; deoxycholic acid	—	
	Bubalus caffer	Cholic acid; chenodeoxycholic acid[c]; deoxycholic acid[c]	Taurine; glycine	U.o.
	Domestic ox	Cholic acid; chenodeoxycholic acid; deoxycholic acid; lithocholic acid; $3\alpha,12\alpha$-dihydroxy-7-oxo-, $7\alpha,12\alpha$-dihydroxy-3-oxo-, 3α-hydroxy-7,12,-dioxo- and 3α-hydroxy-12-oxo-cholanic acids; sapocholic acid; sterocholic acid	Taurine; glycine	
	Gemsbok, Oryx beisa	Allocholic acid[c]; cholic acid[c]; chenodeoxycholic acid[c]; deoxycholic acid		U.o.; Tammar (1966): allocholic acid; cholic acid
	Blesbok, Damaliscus albifrons	Allocholic acid; cholic acid; chenodeoxycholic acid[c]; deoxycholic acid[c]	Taurine; glycine	As above
	Antelope	Cholic acid; deoxycholic acid	—	

* Where not given in Haslewood (1962 or 1964). U.o. refers to unpublished observations in the author's laboratory.

105

APPENDIX—*continued*

Higher class of animal	Species	Bile alcohols or acids isolated from bile	Type of conjugate	References *
	Oribi, *Ourebia ourebi*	Allocholic acid; cholic acid; chenodeoxycholic acid[e]; deoxycholic acid[e]	Taurine; glycine	*U.o.*; Tammar (1966): allocholic acid; cholic acid
	Gerenuk, *Lithocranius walleri*	Allocholic acid[e]; cholic acid[e]; chenodeoxycholic acid[e]; deoxycholic acid[e]	Taurine; glycine (trace)	As above
	Gazelle, *Gazella bennetti*	Cholic acid; chenodeoxycholic acid[e]; deoxycholic acid[e]	Taurine; glycine	*U.o.*
	Gazella rufifrons	Cholic acid; deoxycholic acid[e]	Taurine; glycine (trace)	*U.o.*
	Musk ox, *Ovibos moschatus*	Cholic acid; deoxycholic acid	Taurine; glycine	
	Tahr, *Hemitragus jemlahicus*	Cholic acid; deoxycholic acid[e]	Taurine; glycine	*U.o.*
	Domestic goat	Cholic acid; chenodeoxycholic acid; deoxycholic acid	Taurine; glycine	
	Grecian wild goat	Cholic acid[e]; deoxycholic acid[e]	Taurine; glycine	*U.o.*
	Domestic sheep	Cholic acid; chenodeoxycholic acid; deoxycholic acid	Taurine; glycine	
	Mouflon, *Ovis musimon*	Allocholic acid[e]; cholic acid; deoxycholic acid	Taurine; glycine	*U.o.*; Tammar (1966): allocholic acid

* Where not given in Haslewood (1962 or 1964). *U.o.* refers to unpublished observations in the author's laboratory.

NOTES TO APPENDIX

Except for reptiles, the reader should not perhaps give the same weight to the zoological classification in this Appendix as he would to the classifications in systematic texts. In the main, however, recognized published works have been followed as far as possible, especially Simpson (1945), Romer (1945), Norman (1951) and for Japanese fishes, Okada (1955; 1959/60). For reptiles the author acknowledges with gratitude the valuable advice of Dr Garth Underwood of the British Museum (Natural History).

Acknowledgements

Permission to quote unpublished observations was given by Dr. Ezra Staple and by Mr A. R. Tammar.

Without the generous help of many zoologists, most of the observations could never have been made. The author is especially grateful to Dr W. C. Osman Hill and Mr R. N. T-W-Fiennes (of the Zoological Society of London), Dr Carl Gans and Dr Garth Underwood for considerable collections.

Generous financial help was given by the National Institutes of Health, Bethesda, U.S.A.

REFERENCES TO APPENDIX

Amimoto *et al.* (1965) *see* References to Table 2.4.
Amimoto, K. (1966) *J. Biochem. Tokyo.* **59**, 340.
Danielsson & Einarsson (1964) *see* References to Chapter Five.
Dean & Whitehouse (1966) *see* References to Table 2.4.
Haslewood, G. A. D. (1962). In *Comparative Biochemistry* Ed. M. Florkin & H. S. Mason. Vol. IIIA. New York: Academic Press.
Haslewood, G. A. D. (1964) *Biol. Rev.* **39**, 537.
Norman, J. R. (1951) *A History of Fishes.* 4th Edn. London: Ernest Benn.
Okada, Y. (1955) *Fishes of Japan.* Tokyo: Maruzen Co.
Okada, Y. (1959/60) *Studies on the Freshwater Fishes of Japan,* University of Mie Tsu, Mie Prefecture, Japan.
Romer, A. S. (1945) *Vertebrate Paleontology,* 2nd Edn. Chicago: The University of Chicago Press.
Schoenfield, L. J. & Sjövall, J. (1966) *Acta chem. Scand.* **20**, 1297.
Simpson, G. G. (1945) *Bull. Am. Mus. nat. Hist.* **85**.
Tammar, A. R. (1966) *Biochem. J.* **98**, 25P.
Van den Oord, A., Danielsson, H. & Ryhage, R. (1965) *J. biol. Chem.* **240**, 2242.
Yamasaki, K., Usui, T., Iwata, T., Nakasone, S., Hozumi, M. & Takatsuki S-i. (1965) *Nature, Lond.* **205**, 1326.
Yukawa, M. (1965) *Hiroshima J. med. Sci.* **14**, 1.

Index

N.B. *Species listed systematically in the Appendix are not, in general, re-listed in the Index.*